BEING CHRISTIAN IN YOUR MEDICAL PRACTICE

BEING CHRISTIAN IN YOUR MEDICAL PRACTICE

DR. JIM HALLA

AMBASSADOR INTERNATIONAL
GREENVILLE, SOUTH CAROLINA & BELFAST, NORTHERN IRELAND

www.ambassador-international.com

Being Christian Your Medical Practice

Printed in the United States of America

ISBN: 978-1-62020-022-3
eISBN: 978-1-62020-024-7

Cover Design & Page Layout by Matthew Mulder

AMBASSADOR INTERNATIONAL
Emerald House
427 Wade Hampton Blvd.
Greenville, SC 29609, USA
www.ambassador-international.com

AMBASSADOR BOOKS
The Mount
2 Woodstock Link
Belfast, BT6 8DD, Northern Ireland, UK
www.ambassador-international.com

The colophon is a trademark of Ambassador

I truly don't know how the Lord will use this book. I trust He will — in His own timing. I do not regret the labor spent in all that is involved in writing and publishing of the book. I do believe that God has filled my heart and mind to spread His Kingdom thus furthering His glory and the good of His people. My prayer is that the book will a blessing to physician and patient alike; that it may be the first in a line of many and improved treatises on being Christian in one's medical practice; and that God will be glorified in the reading and application of it.

I offer this from Calvin and Augustine as a summary of my thoughts: "I count myself one of the number of those who write as they learn and learn as they write."

Contents

Preface

YOU MAY WONDER WHETHER THIS book is really *needed*. Over the years of practicing medicine, I have been faced with the issue of how I as a Christian should practice medicine. As a result of continuing to care for patients, interacting with colleagues, observing changes in the medical scene, surveying literature on the subject of the "Christian physician," and (foremost) changes in me, I concluded that something more needed to be written. Consider the number of whys that led to this conclusion:

1. **The practice of medicine is rapidly changing, and further change seems inevitable. Here are some examples:**
   - The looming manpower shortage in the face of an increasing patient load that may be filled by nurse practitioners and physician assistants, so-called "mid levels"
   - The manner in which patients are seen by physicians

- The infringement on the intimacy of the doctor-patient relationship
- The manner in which physicians will be reimbursed
- The continued rise in purported scientific and technological advancements and their use, further enhancing a reliance—even a "dependency"—on them, in part, to protect ourselves from lawsuits

Taken together, these examples indicate that the practice of medicine will *never* be the same as it was in the past. What better time, then, to consider the basic questions posed by this book? What place does Christianity hold in medicine? And if it is significant at all, should you and I become aware of it and know how to implement it in the daily practice in which we engage? Should the Christian physician function as a minister/shepherd and view his patients as "sheep" to be cared for?

2. **The religious climate in the USA is characterized by uncertainty. I went online and put "survey: religious beliefs" in a search engine and encountered a plethora of information. Here are some of the important results from one such report (*USA Today*; "Survey: More have dropped dogma for spirituality in U.S." July 2, 2008):**

> "The survey finds that U.S. adults believe overwhelmingly (92%) in God, and 58% say they pray at least once a day. But the study's authors say that there's a 'stunning'

lack of alignment between people's beliefs and practices and their professed faith. Among the highlights:

- 78% say there are 'absolute standards of right and wrong,' but only 29% rely on their religion to delineate these standards.
- 68% say 'there is more than one way to interpret the teachings of my religion.'
- 51% have a certain belief in a personal God, but 27% are less certain of this; 14% call God an 'impersonal force,' and 5% reject any kind of God."

What are we to make of these figures? The author concluded that "Religion today in the USA is a salad bar where people heap on upbeat beliefs they like and often leave the veggies—like strict doctrines—behind." And "there's a stunning lack of alignment between people's beliefs or practices and their professed faiths." How many of these responders defined themselves as Christian was not given. Nevertheless, it seems that many Americans who call themselves religious go to church but have a "disconnect" between professing and practicing their religion. Is the same true for those who call themselves Christian? Is it possible that, in the area of medicine, many people have relegated the Bible (thus functioning as if God is irrelevant) to "just another book" or to no book at all? Is the Bible no longer a practical or a sufficient guide for daily life?

On the physician side, a recent article, "Survey on Physicians' Religious Beliefs Shows Majority Faithful," purported to be the first study of its type, found that ninety percent of doctors in the United States attend religious services at least occasionally, compared to eighty-one percent of all adults. Fifty-five percent of doctors say their religious beliefs influence how they practice medicine. Interestingly, while more than eighty percent of patients describe themselves as Protestant or Catholic, only sixty percent of physicians come from either group.[1] It seems that being religious has a diverse meaning, and it is not necessarily equated with Christianity.

After reviewing this and other similar reports, I wonder what the Christian church is doing to teach and encourage physicians to be God's kind of doctor. You may ask if the church should have such a role. I would answer in the affirmative based on such passages as Ephesians 4:11-14 and Colossians 1:28-29.[2] The church is to teach and help its mem-

---

1   "Survey on Physicians' Beliefs Shows Majority Faithful": *The University of Chicago Chronicle*, July 14, 2005; vol. 24, #19

2   Ephesians 4:11-14: It was he who gave some to be apostles, some to be prophets, some to be evangelists, and some to be pastors and teachers, to prepare God's people for works of service, so that the body of Christ may be built up, until we all reach unity in the faith and in knowledge of the Son of God and become mature attaining to the whole measure of the fullness

bers to mature as God's kind of people. Clearly, there must be some role. Specifically, what role does it play in preparing both physician and patient to deal with so-called medical issues? How does it help in providing not only encouragement but also direction in these all-important matters? Although I have written minimally on both of these subjects, something more substantial is needed.[3] I am not necessarily suggesting that the church should single out physicians for such teaching but that the church's teaching should so affect, direct, and even comfort Christian physicians to practice medicine God's way for His glory.

There are at least two organizations that have attempted to address being Christian in your medical practice: 1) The National Association of Nouthetic Counselors (NANC) and 2) the Christian Medical and Dental Association (CMDA). NANC has sponsored several conferences addressing the issue

---

of Christ. Then we will no longer be infants tossed back and forth by the waves, and blown here and there by every wind of teaching and by the cunning and craftiness of men in their deceitful scheming. Colossians 1:28-29: We proclaim him, admonishing and teaching everyone with all wisdom, that we may present everyone perfect in Christ. To this end I labor, struggling with all his energy, which so powerfully works in me.

3   These two books are available from Timeless Texts and Redeemer Presbyterian Church in Moore, SC: *True Competence in Medicine: Practicing Biblically-Based Medicine in a Fallen World*: 2005, and *A Biblical Approach to Receiving Medical Care*: 2008.

of being Christian in one's medical practice, but those conferences were held years ago, and they did not address newer issues that I intend to mention in this book. The CMDA has yearly conferences and offers many publications that attempt to describe the "Christian Physician." And *The Journal of Biblical Ethics in Medicine* published articles addressing the "Christian Physician." In my view, all of these attempts, though valuable in part, are either outdated or inadequate. They have not done what needs to be done for God's church and His people today.

In my own practice of some twenty-five years, I have never had a Christian patient ask me how he could be a good steward of his body in order to please God, nor have I had one ask me to help him use his medical condition to do so. In addition, I have rarely heard a sermon (or even sermon illustrations) addressing either of these topics. Moreover, I don't recall ever hearing physicians discuss these subjects among themselves or with me. The whole issue of functioning as God's kind of physician and patient is neglected. I wonder:

- Do *Christian* physicians and patients think differently from their non-believing friends? And if so, how and why?
- Do physicians utilize their gift of new life that they have through saving faith to function as God's kind of physician? Do they know what God's kind of physician is?

And if not, what would utilizing it look like in the office? What is their source for knowing or not knowing?

- Do Christian physicians expect the patient's faith commitment to benefit or hinder the patient when it comes to taking care of his body, or do they even consider the matter?
- Do Christian physicians expect their faith commitment to motivate them to bring biblical-specific principles to bear on the care of their patients?
- Do Christian physicians know how to determine a patient's faith commitment and help him apply a faith-in-action plan in regard to being God's kind of patient?

Too often, believing patients function as do non-believing patients. Because I have an earnest desire for Christian physicians to practice medicine in a way that offers their patients medical care as God's kind of patient, I am writing this book. I trust that not only seasoned doctors but also other medical practitioners and medical students as well will read and consider its message.

3. **Medical schools are the only institutions in our society that produce physicians. Consider these statements from a recent article (*Annals of Internal Medicine* 2010; 152:818-819).**

   "As citizens and policymakers reconsider the U.S. health care system and seek 'quality, affordable health care' for every American, the nature of the physician workforce is becoming a key concern. Many people believe that medical schools are accountable to society for their actions and accomplishments. Beyond their general educational mission, medical schools are expected to train physicians to take care of the population as a whole…."

Such comments raise two questions:

- What type of education do prospective students receive?
- Are they being trained *and* being discipled anywhere, in *any* medical school, about how to be Christian in their medical practice?

In order to answer these questions, we must know what God says about being a Christian in medical practice. The above quotation, which is doubtlessly accurate, plainly indicates that no such training exists. And, if training was available, would—and should—Christian physicians and/or patients be satisfied with it? Moreover, who would teach? What textbooks and other sources would he use? What doctrinal point of view would be taught? And a corollary issue is this: should the church be involved, directly and/or indirectly, in the educative process? These issues are more reasons for my attempt to rectify the situation.

A survey of the information taught by the faculties of various medical schools would be useful in determining what medical students are being exposed to. As one reads the medical literature, one is struck by the glaring absence of anything even resembling a Christian worldview.[4] Evolutionary thinking is one example of the lack of a Christian perspective for giving and receiving medical care. Other examples that exemplify the culture's naturalism include a dependency on non-Christian theories regarding death and dying, doubtful explanations of why things are as they are in the world, and the way that patients are subjectively labeled with a condition. These are just some of the reasons that convinced me that not only "something more" but something radically different is needed.

Why should medical schools teach religion? One dictionary definition of religion is:

- A belief in a divine or superhuman power to be obeyed and worshipped
- Any specific system of belief, worship, or conduct often involving a code of ethics

---

4   *The Rheumatologist*: September 2010, vol. 4, number 9, page 6: "The Bullet of Nature: Whether it is disease or delays, fate works in mysterious ways;" DS Pisetsky; *Practical Pain Management*, September 2010; vol. 10, issue 7, page 12: "Selecting an Antidepressant for Pain Patients;" JE Mack and RR Reeves

- A state of mind or way of life expressing love for and trust in God[5]

If any of these elements is even nearly accurate, how is it that we fail to believe such matters are necessary in practicing medicine? The Christian Scriptures teach, for instance, that all of life is theological (religious), and everyone is a theologian (has religious beliefs, whether true or false). Further, the Bible teaches that man is an inside-out person—from his heart. Simultaneously, every person operates in a vertical and horizontal dimension. Therefore, "doctoring" and being a patient are theological activities. Do doctors believe this? If so (or not so), how do their beliefs affect their practice? The issues, then, are: what does one believe, and what is the source of his beliefs? If asked, one would likely give answers that are vague and varied, calling once again for the sort of specific direction and guidance that this text aims to provide.

On the basis of my Christian faith, I have to conclude that all teaching is inescapably religious because man was created a dependent, religious, worshipping being responsible to God in every facet of his life. Erroneously (even irrationally), supposed neutrality in regard to religion is widely affirmed; medicine as now practiced in the United States is considered non-religious although it involves "oughts" and "shoulds." These decidedly

5   *Webster's New Universal Unabridged Dictionary,* Deluxe 2nd edition, Simon and Schuster, New York, NY, 1979, page 1527.

moral and religious terms, however, are anything but neutral. Man can't escape who he is or the God who made him. He *is* religious! Medical schools, as well as all teaching institutions, teach a form of religion—whether they know it or not. If the institution is avowedly non-Christian, then it teaches the religion of secular humanism (see footnote 4 in which Pisetsky speaks of "fate"). If not avowedly so, the result (unknowingly or not) is likely not to be significantly different.

The Christian worldview is a chain of linked truths, among which are doctrines about God, man, sin, salvation, Christ, the Holy Spirit, and the church. The links hold together only as strongly as their weakest link. Therefore, it is impossible for any school to teach a truly Christian world-and-life view of medicine unless the entire faculty is fully Christian. That, of course, is more than one could ask at this stage, but a beginning must be made somewhere. At the very least, a book such as this one attempts to correct false views of Christianity in medicine and attempts to stir up enough interest that, in time, something will be done to change the emphasis in at least some schools of medicine.

4. **The expected arrival of the DSM-5 has been projected for 2014. There has been much written regarding its advent. Some highly acclaim its arrival, while others are concerned about it, and still others are reserved in their comments. My rationale for mentioning its ex-**

pected arrival is captured in the following quotation (*JAMA* 2010;303:1974-1975):

> One of the goals of the *JAMA* commentary, say the authors, is to highlight for physicians several major goals of the *DSM-5* process, *including facilitating further integration of psychiatry into mainstream medical practice* (italics mine), looking at the challenges of diagnosing mental disorders in general medical settings, and emphasizing the importance of attending to patients with mental disorders regardless of the clinician's medical specialty.

No matter what your thoughts on a "psychological" approach to handling problems of life may be (and you should have a biblical one), you should be aware that apparently there is a push by one segment of the "medical" community to integrate its views and practice paradigms into mainstream medical practice. Why psychiatry? Why not Christianity? You and I must determine whether a psychological approach in the practice of medicine will help or hinder being Christian in our medical practice. For the Christian, that decision may well be the final determiner of whether he adopts the reasoning behind the DSM-5. Indeed, it is important for every Christian to have a clear idea of the place (if any) of secular psychological principles in his life. That, too, is a matter for discussion later in the book.

5. In my own metamorphoses, I have been a board-certi-
   fied rheumatologist for about thirty-five years. I have
   held a faculty position at the University of Alabama in
   Birmingham, have labored as a physician, have taught,
   have done research, and have authored a number of
   scientific and clinical articles.[6] I have been in private
   practice for almost thirty years. Overall, I enjoy the
   practice of medicine, and I appreciate what I can offer
   my patients for controlling disease and improving their
   ability to function. Specifically, let me mention a few
   kudos of modern medicine in the field of rheumatology. There has been development in immunogenetics;
   growth in the area of immunology, biochemistry, car-
   tilage, collagen, and bone physiology; the production
   and use of biological agents in the treatment of some
   rheumatic diseases; and sophisticated technological
   advances that have improved diagnosis and treatment
   options. I appreciate God's providence in allowing me
   to witness them and use them in the care of patients.

   However, I can also say that I have encountered changes in

---

6   My curriculum vitae is on file and open for inspection. In part, I was
involved in clinical research and blessed to have an active and more-than-
competent group of basic science researchers on hand for in-depth studies
that helped to explain various clinical observations of several rheumatic
diseases.

the practice, delivery, and philosophy of medicine that I consider potentially questionable. These include the access and delivery system of medical care, the proliferation of medications and drugs often resulting in polypharmacy, and technological advances both in terms of diagnosis and treatment strategies resulting in a presumed growing ability to explain and classify symptoms, thus resulting in labeling patients with various syndromes, illnesses, and diseases but failing to heal them.

In addition, I have changed. Now as I care for patients, I note *how* patients respond to their various health problems. I observe how their relationship (or non-relationship) with Jesus Christ impacts them as patients. In all patients it has some positive or negative impact. Unfortunately, their slight interest makes little difference in their treatment and its effects. But that is to be expected; not everyone appreciates the work of Jesus Christ. Moreover, my own labors as a rheumatologist were formerly carried out as an unbeliever, but in the last twenty-five years I have been practicing as a Christian. Initially after becoming a believer, however, what I was in Christ did not influence how I practiced rheumatology. Then, gradually, all that changed. Though not quickly, I began to take Scripture seriously and tried to apply it to all of my life, including my medical practice. Now I consider my practice of medicine a ministry to my patients for their benefit and God's glory. Surprisingly (though it should not have been), I found that the practice of medicine became more simplified when I did so, even though everything all around me seemed much more complex. I shall explain this seeming incongruity later on.

Hopefully, you are curious and intrigued enough at this point to continue reading further. I have several thoughts that I think will be of interest to you.

CHAPTER 1

Worldview and Purpose

LIKE ALL PRACTICING PHYSICIANS, I daily observe patients, nurses, physicians, and other health care providers. Many (perhaps, most) are "doing the best they can." The patient *receives* and the physician *gives* medical care. But I have also noted *how* those decisions about giving and receiving medical care are based on one's worldview. I have observed the struggles, often dissatisfaction, futility, and ultimate bondage of patients and physicians that result when principles of biblical truth are ignored, are insufficiently or inconsistently applied, or are integrated only as "another" way to get relief or maintain "good" health. I have concluded that it is one's religious worldview which affects the giving and receiving of health care so as to produce significant results.

This brings us to a major two-fold consideration: just what is the purpose of the practice of medicine? A subsidiary consideration is how we shall obtain an answer to the question.

Another major matter is determining just what the Christian physician's responsibility to patients is. Is he required to pursue religious ministry? If so, what sort? Considering some foundational truths will enable us to begin to answer many other questions such as:

- What is implied by the fact that God is the self-existent, self-contained Originator, Creator, and Owner of His creation, *including man*? Because truth in medicine is vital, a Christian believes that it is important to know that all truth finds its ultimate existence in God. How does that fact affect medical practice?

- What is implied by the fact that man is not God, and he exists because God exists? God created man a being wholly dependent upon Him for his very life and how he lives it.

- This life when lived out to its fullest begins vertically— in a proper relationship to God. What are the implications for the practice of medicine that life is theological and everyone is a theologian (a good or a bad one)? Man functions according to his theology, either in or out of a proper relationship to God. What are the consequences of a failure to recognize this?

- What is said of man's being is also said of his knowledge. Just as man's being is derived from God, so also is his knowledge. He knows because God knows, but (unlike God) he knows with creaturely knowledge which is limited, finite, and derived. And because of man's sin, his capacity to reason is limited, erroneous, and distorted. How do these truths impact the practice of medicine?

- Man was created a moral, ethically responsible being. How should that truth influence the giving and receiving of medical care?

These truths (to be explicated further as we continue, but pondered at the moment) presuppose an absolute God who plans all things and has been working out His plans throughout history. This providential working includes the specifics of your daily life and *all* that you do in your medical office. Since God is the ultimate reference point for all of life, that includes the practice of medicine in all aspects. Help, and giving help, *must* be defined and applied according to God's standard, the Scriptures: "In him we were also chosen, having been predestined according to the plan of him who works out everything in conformity with the purpose of his will" (Ephesians 1:11). The Bible offers limited, but inerrant knowledge concerning such help which we shall explore and set forth in time.

Here, it is imperative to draw your attention to the absolute necessity of a standard for truth and for life. God made man to be under His authority, but man seeks independence from God (too often, even the believer functions this way). He is ignorant of or repudiates God's standard. But he cannot avoid the issue of the need for a standard. Every person relies on some standard (knowingly or otherwise). For the believer, his standard for faith and life is the Bible. Consider these general, profound truths regarding the Bible taught in 2 Timothy 3:15-17 and 2 Peter 1:19-21:

> . . . *and how from infancy you have known the holy Scriptures which are able to make you wise unto salvation. All Scripture is God-breathed and is useful for teaching, rebuking, correcting, and training in righteousness so that the man of God may be thoroughly equipped for every good work*
>
> (2 Timothy 3:15-17).

> *His divine power has given us everything we need for life and godliness through our knowledge of him who called us by his own glory and goodness. Through these he has given us his very great and precious promises so that through them you may participate in the divine nature and escape the corruption in the world caused by evil desires*
>
> (2 Peter 1:3-4).

- The Bible is God's Word, infallible and authoritative, in written form.

- Believing and applying it makes all the difference in what one does as a physician—or patient.

- The Bible is unlike any other book. In it, God voluntary condescended to speak to man in spite of his sin. Why? He did so, among other reasons, for man's benefit (including that of patients as well as doctors).

- It is light—God's light, throwing light upon every fact of life, including physical problems and their solutions, in order for them to be understood.

- It is God's powerful, purposeful self-expression by which He creates, controls, and directs as well as defines and interprets. As such, it reveals principles for living a victorious life here and throughout eternity.

- It is the voice of God–His self communication and self disclosure to His creatures. Moreover, in it He analyzes and discusses man and His world. He explains creation, providence, salvation, and personal sanctification. An understanding of the process of sanctification, for instance, is a pivotal feature of being Christian in your medical practice. Frankly, failure to understand sanctification and how it affects the practice of medicine is appalling.

- The Bible, in its original manuscripts, is the very Word of God. It is His Word as truly as if it had been spoken audibly to you by God. If God were to speak audibly now, He would say nothing more, nothing less, and nothing different from what He has already said. If He was right here speaking audibly, He would say exactly what He has said in His written Word—though probably in a more contemporary mode and language.

- The Bible is the very Word of God. To distrust or disobey it is to distrust or disobey God.

What is the upshot of the above truths? Our understanding of Scripture is intended to influence *every* aspect of life, including the practice of medicine and the functioning of a Christian physician (the same fact applies to the patient).

Consider the above truths in light of the answer I most commonly hear regarding the *purpose* of the practice of medicine. In some form or fashion, the answer most often given is "to give good medical care – to give *help*." Rarely, does one define what he means by "help," and the Bible is rarely mentioned even as an aspect of giving help. The word "help" is both a noun and a verb. It is a generic term. The word means "to make it easier for something to exist or for someone to do something." Help, then, has to do with improving the condition of the person through assistance and various sorts of aid. Its goal is comfort. But there is comfort, and there is *comfort*. And, in one sense, that is what this book is all about: distinguishing various sorts of help so that one may be certain that he is providing God's kind of help. Do you know what kind of help and comfort you bring to the office and bedside every day? Does it include Christian truth?

Sometimes the giving of medical help seems rather simple when the diagnosis is straight-forward, and there is an adequate solution such as in the case of tonsillitis, appendicitis, or rheumatoid arthritis (RA). A proper, and even quick, diagnosis enables the doctor to give the correct solution. Here the medical model for disease stands at its best.[7] The concept expressed in that model is that symptoms and signs arise from proven pathology; directed, skillful therapy is required; and often there are good results—either cure or improvement. However, even in the seemingly simple situations described, it is necessary for the Christian physician to function as more than a "body mechanic." If so, how does he do it? By the term "body mechanic," I am referring to a physician whose focus is primarily on the material and physical to explain and deal with symptoms. Consequently, he relies on medication, surgery, procedures, or physical modalities to relieve symptoms. When isolated from Him, these become a physician's medical gods. The spiritual condition of the patient is ignored to the detriment of all involved.

Bear with me as I take you on a brief excursus into the matters of symptoms, signs, and the meaning of body and

7   See Appendix A regarding various models for medical disease and treatment approach

spiritual mechanic. Understanding these concepts is important for giving (and receiving) God's kind of help in the practice of medicine.[8] Symptoms are what people report. They are personal, subjective, and based on how a person feels, his interpretation of those feelings, and his thinking about his body. He then communicates his feelings. A symptom is known, but only because the person tells someone. Symptoms include pain, fatigue, headache, and feverishness. A fever, which is a sign, can be documented, verified, and objectified; it may follow from the complaint of feverishness. A person may complain of feeling feverish (a symptom). The same patient may also have an elevated temperature (a sign). Signs may or may not be reported by the patient, but the point is, they are measurable. For instance, a person with hypertension (a sign) may report no abnormalities (symptoms), but his elevated blood pressure reading tells the doctor that something is wrong *with* the body. Symptoms differ in this respect.

That brings us to another important point. I have found it beneficial to help patients distinguish between something wrong *in* the body and something wrong *with* the body. This concept is linked with symptoms and signs. A symptom such as palpitations (patients report an "irregular and racing heart"

---

8   For a more complete discussion of this subject, see my book: *True Competence in Medicine: Practicing Biblically-Based Medicine in a Fallen World*, especially pages 24-26.

with or without chest discomfort) may actually be due to something wrong *with* the body (such as anemia or thyroid disease). If the patient's heart rate is greater than 100/beats per minute, by definition, he has tachycardia. Now the patient who complained of palpitations—a symptom—has a *sign*: tachycardia. Next, we must determine whether the problem is *with* the body or *in* the body. If the doctor discovers thyroid disease, the problem is *with* the body, and the tachycardia is a sign of pathology: a diseased thyroid gland. If the person has anemia, the tachycardia is a sign of problems *with* the body but the heart is not the problem. The tachycardia is a physiological response to the anemia. There is disease—something is wrong *with* the body—and the symptom led to a medical examination and a correct diagnosis.

Consider another scenario. If the patient is worrying (which, biblically, is a control-trust issue and concern gone wrong) or being fearful (which, biblically, is a control-trust issue and personal responsibility misdirected), his tachycardia probably is not the result of pathology. The tachycardia is a physiological change, not a pathological one. The change is *in* the body, not *with* the body. The patient's body is working the way God designed it to work given the patient's situation and his response to it. As we will discuss later in the book, there is a vital link between a person's thoughts and desires, how his body is working, and how he feels. Faced with the patient who is worrying and fearful, the doctor should tell the patient that the problem is not *with* his body but *in* the body. And, then, he must clarify the distinction. The doctor will gather information on the person's thinking, wanting, feelings, and doing or not doing. The patient at such a stage in his diagnosis and treatment may well be ripe to receive biblical truth in regards to handling life by a biblical response to problems or perceived ones.

Helping patients understand how fearfully and wonderfully they are made is an important matter.[9] However, most don't understand the connections between:

- Thinking and wanting, which are predominantly inner-person activities
- Feelings (which are felt in the body) and doing, (or not doing) which are physical

It seems to me that too often we label a person with a condition that is based purely on subjective factors. In fact, subjectivity seems to have become the final authority even for so-called "evidence-based" medicine.[10] As result

---

9   See Psalm 139:14-16; Ecclesiastes 11:5; 1 Corinthians 6:19-20; 7:23

10   Evidence-based medicine (EBM) apparently has recognized the need for objectivity in diagnosis and treatment, and has added two other factors: clinical expertise and patient values, both loaded with subjectivity! According to D. Sackett, evidence-based medicine is "the conscientious, explicit, and judicious use of current best evidence in making decisions about the care

of Adam's sin and the Fall, all men are sinners and do not think God's thoughts after Him, or desire His desires. Even as believers, subjectivity too often rules our thinking and wanting. When that is the case, the primary goal of a visit to the doctor's office is to obtain relief. Consequently, there is the tendency by both patient and physician to functionally trump the use and application of biblical principles with the practice of "mechanic-based" and "subjectivity-based" medicine.

In more complicated situations, in terms of diagnosis and treatment, the proper help called for is lifestyle changes, including radical ones. Generally, that means exchanging "bad" behaviors (sinful ones from God's perspective)

---

of the individual patient. It means integrating individual clinical expertise with the best available external clinical evidence from systematic research." Further, Sackett says that EBM is the integration of clinical expertise, patient values, and the best evidence into the decision making process for patient care. Clinical expertise refers to the clinician's cumulated experience, education, and clinical skills. The patient brings to the encounter his or her own personal and unique concerns, expectations, and values. The best evidence is usually found in clinically relevant research that has been conducted using sound methodology. D.R. Bordley writes that EBM "converts the abstract exercise of reading and appraising the literature into the pragmatic process of using the literature to benefit individual patients while simultaneously expanding the clinician's base." This information is taken from the website, *www.hsl.unc.edu/lm/ebm/whatis.htm.*

for "good" behaviors and lifestyles that are conducive to achieving relief or improving bodily functions. In fact, both medical science and God's Word call for these changes. Which one will you emphasize and why? Your Christian responsibility is first to honor God—not medical science. Science is not neutral; it explains some of God's activity in His universe, and so it should honor God. The patient is to make so-called lifestyle changes in order to please God as His kind of steward—not primarily to seek relief or maintain health. When medical care is reduced to the level of mere relief under the banner of medical science, the Christian physician has missed his opportunity to function as a good biblical theologian-practitioner. He has neither demonstrated to his patient Christ's place in his well-being or the proper manner of glorifying God in his illness. God created and designed the body, and He has given directions for its care. When the Christian physician helps his patient honor God by what the patient does and does not do, that is a radically different sort of "help." And, of course, what the physician (and the patient) thinks (or doesn't think) about life, his body, and the God of that body, either pleases and honors God or it doesn't. Both patient and the physician will benefit immensely from a genuine biblical-theological medical practice.

On the other hand, the Christian physician must avoid

functioning as a "spiritual mechanic." By this, I mean one who has cut, separated, and dichotomized man into parts; man is neither dichotomistic nor trichotomistic but duplex. The "spiritual mechanic" divides the person into spiritual-physical, and he primarily addresses the spiritual side of man. An important note, "spiritual" (today) is not always (or usually) defined as Holy Spirit-centered-and-directed (Please see Appendix A for further discussion of this subject). The spiritual mechanically-oriented Christian physician will use biblical truth, and even prayer, much like medication. This often takes the form of encouraging more faith (often more prayer) or perhaps being evangelistic and "getting the patient saved." The concern here is that, once saved, what does the person do? "Being saved" is the start. Now the saved person must do something. Such should be the emphasis of the Christian physician as he cares for believers. Specifically, given the situation, what biblical principles do you bring to him to help him get victory in the problem? And victory must be defined God's way. It is growing in the situation, not necessarily getting out of it, by issuing the unpleasantness and uncertainty to become more like Christ.

In order for the Christian physician to function neither as a "physical" nor as a "spiritual mechanic," he should free his thinking from such polarities—especially if it has been

captured by the Greek word "psychosomatic." Rather, he
will be able to think and speak correctly about the problem as spiritual–physiological.[11] Responses to unpleasant
situations result in symptoms, and maybe signs, that are
best characterized as spiritual–physiological. The response
to any circumstance is spiritual as well as physical; it is
an inner-person response based on thinking and wanting
that produces physiological changes in the body. The term
spiritual-physiological is based on God's creational design of
man, and it encompasses proper "duplex theology." Scripture describes man as a duplex creature: united in body
and soul. He is both physical and spiritual; a whole person
who thinks, desires, and acts at all times according to what
is in his heart. Scripturally, the "heart" is the real you, your
inner life lived before God and yourself. It is the inner core
of a person's being by which he thinks, purposes, desires,
motivates, and concludes (see especially Proverbs 4:23; Acts
8:22; Romans 10:6-10; Hebrews 3:12). The heart includes
both affections and intellect. It is like a storehouse from
which actions and behavior spring so that it can be said that

11   See *The Christian Counselor's Medical Desk Reference*, Robert D.
Smith, Timeless Texts, 2000, page 42-43. A person's response to a situation
is spiritual (from the inside – his heart) and this affects the body's physiology. The person's response to problems invariably produces symptoms and
perhaps may "produce" disease (however defined).

a person lives out of his heart (Matthew 6:19-21; 12:34-35; 15:18-19; Mark 7:20; Luke 6:43-45). What a person thinks and desires is his motivation for all that he does.

Wrongly, some (perhaps most) Christian physicians fail to treat the person as a unit—a whole person. The patient is considered to have physical needs or diseases that the Bible doesn't address, thereby functionally excluding God and His truth (biblical principles) from true help. On the other hand, the physician may understand that a patient's symptoms are related purely to "psychological" or "spiritual" problems. If that is the case, he will treat based on that "diagnosis," and he will fail to explain that biblical truths relate to his body problem. Or possibly, he will present these biblical truths incorrectly.

As a word of caution, Christians must be discriminating when using the term "*holistic.*" By this term, the secular community means that since man is and can be compartmentalized and can be parceled out to multiple health care providers— doctor, social worker, nurse, and psychologist—somehow, thereby, we treat him totally. In fact, the secular view of "holistic" medicine is in stark contrast to God's creational design of man who is a unified duplex being. Ironically, in the current holistic view, in order to minister to the whole person, he must first be "cut up." We will continue our discussion of the application of this most important truth for the practice of medicine later.

Another issue is determining what standard to use in determining what true "help" and true "comfort" is. Mostly, physicians (as I said) think in terms of relief. The Bible has much to say about receiving and giving help as God's *Owner's Manual* for life (see pages 10 and 41 for discussion re: 2 Timothy 3:15-17; 2 Peter 1:3-4). The biblical term for "help" as we have said is a large one. It includes comfort, instruction, and assistance. Again, we must consult *God's* standard to know what those words mean to Him and how He expects us to administer help. If He expects His people to understand what help means *from His perspective*, it is reasonable, then, to ask:

- According to His standard, how does He define help?
- Are my motivation and goals for giving help in accordance with God's?

The Bible speaks volumes in regard to these matters. For instance, one passage among many is 2 Corinthians 1:3-4:

> *Praise be to the God and Father of our Lord Jesus Christ, the Father of compassion and the God of all comfort, who comforts us in all our troubles, so that we can comfort those in any trouble with comfort we ourselves have received from God.*
>
> (2 Corinthians 1:3-4)

Based on these verses, Scripture depicts two groups of

people: comforters/helpers and comfortees/helpees. Every believer, doctors included, is both a helper and in need of help. This is because of God's creational design of man. Before sin, perfect Adam was in "need" of communion with God, the only source of true help. Man has always "needed" God. But man, as God's image bearer, has been severely marred by sin, seeking help as he defines it from any source other than God. And try as one might, he can't escape the fact that he is, at once, both a helper and helpee, and that true help comes only from God. God's expectations as defined in Scripture allow for no neutrality in the matter. If one is not practicing medicine for God, he is practicing against Him. Elsewhere, the Bible dispels the myth of neutrality in such passages as Matthew 12:30; Luke 9:50; 11:23, Joshua 24:14-15, and 1 Kings 18:21. In God's world—including medical offices—neutrality is a myth. Indeed, the idea of neutrality is a particular kind of bias that is underlaid by a negative attitude toward God. It behooves both physician and patient, therefore, to understand God's views both of help and comfort. One purpose of the book is to spell out what true comfort is and how to give it.

The Christian physician can be God's kind of comforter in a number of ways. Listening and speaking as a caring, compassionate helper is a source of encouragement: "He who answers before listening–that is his folly and his shame" (Proverbs 18:13); "The heart of the discerning acquires knowledge and the ears of the wise seek it out" (Proverbs 18:15). Scripture says that answering before listening is playing the fool. Listening to learn may be the best help you can give at a particular moment. But true help rarely ever stops at listening; listening must go somewhere: "The wise in heart are called discerning, and pleasant words promote instruction" (Proverbs 16:21); "A wise man's heart guides his mouth, and his lips promote instruction" (Proverbs 16:23). The wise doctor will listen to learn, in part, to promote biblically-directed medical instruction. Patients present with varying complaints and concerns. The diagnosis may be uncertain; humanly speaking, the future appears bleak. Or the diagnosis may be certain, but the course and treatment may be drawn out. In each case, good listening always "sets the table" for the Christian physician to learn where the patient is in his relationship to God. He does so in order to promote truth for His glory and for the benefit of the patient. I present examples of "how-tos" throughout the book and especially in the last chapter, so stay tuned!

Believing physicians seem content in their practice when saying things like:

- I am a Christian who practices medicine, and that makes it OK.
- Treating people and making them feel better is really what it is all about.
- And with manpower shortages and insurance changes,

there are plenty of people who need to be seen and cared for.

- So what else can be expected of me?

However, a lingering question and a constant refrain for me is this: Exactly how do biblical principles fit into the training and practice of physicians and medical personnel? And, if they don't fit, why don't they? Much more needs to be said about practicing medicine as a Christian. Consider the following principles and questions:

- In John 8:31-32, Jesus said, "The truth will set you free." Can you define the patient's bondage biblically, define "truth" and "free," the standard for defining it, how to declare it, and how to apply God's truth to the patient in his situation? If not, your present practice probably needs changing.

- Being a doctor and going to the doctor are theological issues. How does your theology govern your decisions at present? Can you define your theology clearly?

- A "de-medicalization" of physicians is necessary and should be replaced by a "*Scripto-centric*" approach to life in the practice of medicine. Radical? Of course! Ours is a God who has given much *to* us and expects much *of* us.

- There is a biblical view of the practice of medicine. And it is the major avenue that patients have for reaching true comfort and help. You must, therefore, be able to articulate it.

- A rightly understood biblical view of medicine is the only way that doctors have for giving genuine hope to hurting people and of advancing the kingdom of God.

CHAPTER 2

The Christian Doctor

ASCERTAINING THE "WHAT" AND THE "how" of being a Christian medical doctor can be addressed in a variety of ways. In fact, various groups *have* addressed this subject. One approach is to do "door-to-door" research. Before writing this book, I asked a number of local physicians who had the reputation for being Christians to fill out a questionnaire (see Appendix B). My goal was to get a "flavor" of Christian thinking as it is related to the practice of medicine. It made sense to familiarize myself with a sample of the prevailing attitudes and practice habits. As a result, I uncovered some thought-provoking facts.

Most of the physicians were very much aware that being a Christian must have an impact on their medical practice. The majority defined "being a Christian physician" as tantamount to "sending a Christian message" in their office. For most, "sending a Christian message" meant practicing good medicine (I left the definition of the principal terms open to the responder. Obviously, the concepts of "a Christian medical practice" and "good medicine" are critical. I will clarify these terms as we progress through the book). The physicians I interviewed thought that sending a Christian message included being compassionate, caring, merciful, and honest when interacting with patients and office staff. No one mentioned it, but apparently this Christlike demeanor enabled these physicians to see a number of demanding patients who left the office satisfied. As a whole, it seemed to me that most interviewees were content with the present "what" and "how" of their practice. They voiced the opinion that nothing more seemed to be needed or changed. They were content with the status quo. From my perspective, if this is the norm for Christians, to bring about any change will be a mammoth task.

Many doctors who answered the questionnaire agreed that it was *best* not to "force" their religion on patients. Others spoke in a way that indicated agreement. I wondered at the use of this word. They seemed very concerned about not doing so. Attempts to be neutral seemed to be the prevailing modus operandi. I directly addressed the issue of neutrality on pages 10-11 and 18 when considering the matter of education in medical schools and the concern for giving comfort. There, I wondered, "Is neutrality a goal in medical practice? Is it even a possibility? And if it is achievable, what does it look like, and, of special importance, is it the best approach to the practice of medicine? How would one decide?" Many interviewed considered religion private and personal. Others did not want to "take advantage" of hurting people. And perhaps some may not have known how to present Christ if they thought it wise to do so.

Now, for a moment, consider that word *force*. What did each one mean by *force*? The word has a number of different meanings, including *to compel* and *to motivate*. People motivate by words delivered in a variety of ways, by silence, by action, or by inaction. No interviewee defined the term *force* for me. But if by *force* the responders meant "to tell, cajole, or harp in order to win an argument or to get your way," we can all agree that isn't God's way. God motivates His people from the inside through His Holy Spirit and not from any force from without. In His goodness and mercy He has chosen to do radical "heart" surgery for the purpose of saving His people (Ezekiel 18:31; 36:25-27; John 3:3-8; Acts 16:14; Titus 3:5). As the Invader God, He changes hearts and provides His Holy Spirit who gives His people biblical truth to guide them (John 3:3-8; 6:38-45; 8:31032; 14:6,26; 15:26; 16:13). But it all happens *from within* through changed hearts.

God's "inside" operation results from His irresistible grace. In response to this "*inside* operation," God's people hear His call and follow Him. As a result of the application of God's grace by His Spirit, the believer is a new creature in Christ. As a new creature, he wants to do God's will out of gratitude; he is never forced. This inner compulsion comes from a true sense of what Christ has done for him and a fervent desire to say thank you. He no longer lives for self but endeavors (however imperfectly) to live for God (2 Corinthians 5:14–17). God never forces anyone against his own will. What God wants, the new believer now wants; what God thinks, the new believer will now think when motivated (not forced) by Him.

The believer ministers by providing biblical truth and rationale for its use. Why shouldn't this dynamic be at work in medical offices as well as anywhere else? Indeed, the patient's physical problem provides the ideal context and opening for providing help that extends beyond medicine itself. Presenting biblical principles appropriate to the patient and his medical condition may also be the most caring, healing act that you as a Christian physician perform. How one does so is extremely important, of course. I will give practical how-tos along these lines as we progress.

In my questionnaire, I did not define Christian. I let the responder do that. The answers given in the questionnaire appeared to reflect the major emphasis that is present in the existing literature and what I have overheard physicians say about practicing as a Christian.[12] The emphasis for practicing as a Christian given in all these sources is to emulate Christ in His relationship with people—both with patients and staff. The likeness of Christ is usually said to include compassion and tenderheartedness as a faithful listener and comforter. Interpersonal relationships are emphasized.

As an aside, it would be interesting to study how simply listening to people speak about their complaints is productive. My belief is that such material would be either slim or virtually non-existent and that such an approach would be unproductive—or even counter-productive—to true help. Listening certainly has it place. Good listening is what learners do (1 Peter 3:7). But listening is for learning in order to do apply biblical truth in an effort to solve the problem.

Among physicians and in the literature, exhortations for doctors to be "like Christ, the great Physician" abound; thus, they must seek to represent Christ. Sounds good. But, that provides a major issue. No one defined those phrases. I know that some physicians pray with patients, especially when asked.

---

12   Also, see such articles in the *Journal of Biblical Ethics in Medicine*: vol. 5, page 11, 1991: "Defining the Christian Doctor" by Robert Maddox, MD; vol. 6, page 81, 1992: "Defining a Christian Doctor" by Spiros Lazarou; and various articles from the website of the Christian Medical and Dental Association

Some encourage patients to seek out their pastor and "support groups," including their church family, for various sorts of help. Some doctors are evangelistic, handing out tracts and going on medical missions. And some physicians engage patients to make lifestyle and behavioral changes that will improve their patients' health. What I don't know is how many physicians present biblical truth (not as an alternative source of relief) as a major (even prime) source of help for the believing patient—no matter what his physical condition may be. In particular, I wonder if doctors are helping patients to think and to desire that which is in accordance with biblical injunctions in relation to their physical problems. Indeed, do they have any idea what such injunctions might be?

I turned to the Bible to discover what it said about Jesus as "the Great Physician" and to determine what it meant to model and represent Him. The term *great physician* is not used in Scripture, but Jesus' healing activity is highlighted throughout the Gospels. Consider Matthew, in 4:23 ("Jesus went throughout Galilee teaching in the synagogues, preaching the good news of the kingdom, and healing every disease and sickness among the people"). Matthew emphasized Jesus' three-pronged ministry of teaching, preaching, and supernatural healing. In fact, in terms of physical healing (unlike televangelists of today), Jesus never lost a patient and never had an unsuccessful outcome. Wonderful! Yet, physical healing was not His only or even major concern. Therefore, it is mandatory that we give heed to the other aspects of His ministry.

Twice Jesus referred to Himself as a physician: Luke 4:23 ("And He said to them, 'No doubt you will quote this proverb to Me, "Physician, heal yourself"!'"), and in Matthew 9:12-13 ("But when He heard this, He said, 'It is not those who are healthy who need a physician, but those who are sick. But go and learn what this means, I desire compassion, and not sacrifice, for I did not come to call the righteous but sinners'"). The word He used for *physician* and *doctor* in Greek is *iatros*, a term that is used six times in the New Testament and has a similar meaning as today.[13] It has no special meaning. In these references, however, Jesus was not speaking of practicing medicine. Close examination shows that they have something to say about aspects of His ministry that does impinge upon the practice of medicine. These, though less directly, do bear an influence upon the health of others.

Jesus' healing ministry glorified God. The people could witness physical healing as it occurred. These healings testified to Jesus' compassion and concern for people. They testified to His power and dominion: Jesus' miracles attested to His authority over death, disease, demons, and nature.

---

13   Those places are: Matthew 9:12; Mark 2:17; 5:26; Luke 4:23; 5:31; Colossians 4:14 All refer to Jesus except Colossians 4:14 which refers to Luke.

Granted, He used miraculous power to bring healing about, but as He did, He showed how to deal with medical problems. We read in John 20:30-31:

> *Jesus did many miraculous signs in the presence of his disciples which are not recorded in this book. But these are written that you may believe that Jesus is the Christ, the Son of God, and that by believing you may have life in his name.*

> (John 20:30-31)

The central emphasis of His miraculous healings, then, was to turn people's hearts to the *major* healing that they needed—the change of hard and callous hearts. The people needed what God calls a heart of flesh; one that is soft and receptive to God's directive will and open to the influence of the Holy Spirit as He directs people through Scripture (1 Corinthians 2:4,12-16; Galatians 1:11-12; 1 Thessalonians 1:5-6). Such a heart is one that only God Himself can provide (Ezekiel 36:25-27; John 3:3-8). As Jesus' healings direct us to this fact, so should healing (and the care of patients) today do the same!

These healings, then, were not unrelated to the practice of medicine or the maintenance of health. A significant biblical principle concerning Jesus' healing ministry was that physical healings and physical terms such as *doctor* (rightly understood) *point* to the presence of a greater spiritual reality in addition to mere physical attention. You might even say that man needs an "inside operation." Jesus obviously ministered to the whole (duplex) person. In His healing ministry, it is apparent that Jesus considered that healing also required a deeper spiritual activity (Mark 5:19-21, 34; Luke 17:19). Man needs more than a fixed-up body. His body is not the only, or (often) the main, problem in his medial condition. This fact is contrary to the patient's thinking and unfortunately to that of most doctors'. Jesus' healings ministered to both body and soul, showing that the two are integrally related. The inner (or heart) change that Jesus effected cannot be safely ignored if we wish to minister in a Christlike way (a *truly* holistic manner!).

To represent Christ, and to emulate the Great Physician in your practice of medicine, you too (though not performing miracles) must exhibit a proper, vertical orientation as you minister to your patient. Compassion, concern for both patient and staff, and improvement in the patient's physical well-being of course are necessary, but they are things that (after a sort) even non-believing physicians do. There is, however, one thing that they cannot do. They cannot deal with this inner dimension of human problems the way Jesus did. Jesus still helps Christian physicians who seek His assistance. From looking at Jesus' ministry, it is an obvious fact that healing has a redemptive dimension. Our ministry, of course, is non-redemptive in the sense that *we* don't redeem patients.

We do offer the "derivative" redemption which Jesus achieved by His life and death on the cross. The effects of this are mediated to us by His Holy Spirit who uses Scripture to bring about redemptive help—conformity to Jesus Christ, the true Image of God (Hebrews 1:1-3). Unbelieving physicians, even if attempting to minister to the whole person, do so in a way that is contrary to the Bible and are utterly helpless to provide derivative, redemptive help. It follows that the only logical, biblical recourse for Christian physicians is to address the whole person as the Bible says Jesus did. We do so by casting our entire practice in the spiritual-physiological form mentioned earlier.

Consider several examples of a physical reality pointing to a spiritual truth that is adjacent to it:

- John 4:31-34: Jesus told His disciples that being satisfied was a great thing. The disciples thought in terms of physical eating as the major route to satisfaction, but Jesus emphasized a surpassingly superior way. Jesus said that His "food" was not physical but spiritual. It consisted of doing His Father's will. Jesus experienced a greater sense of pleasure, contentment, and satisfaction from doing the will of His Father than He did from eating food. A physician who understands this fact will be able to provide multi-layered satisfaction for his patients as well as experiencing joy in his work.

- Matthew 9:12; 12:7-14: in verse 12 of chapter 9, Jesus clarifies to whom He came. He came to those who are unclean spiritually. The teachers of Israel claimed both physical and spiritual cleanness could be achieved through ritualistic practices. They did not seek physical or spiritual healing. They were their own doctors, and poor ones! They missed Jesus' point. The issue was not physical but spiritual uncleanness and their total inability to provide it.

Then in chapter 12 verse 7, Jesus said that He healed physically on the Sabbath because God's law demands that inner-man directed activities of mercy and compassion are always proper. Since God doesn't take a day off, neither did Jesus. He told them that they had missed the point of what God called "uncleanness." They thought only of physical healing. Lepers were considered ceremonially unclean because of their skin disease. To them, helping a leper meant focusing solely on the outer person. However, all needed to be healed spiritually in addition to the physical infirmities they had. If the Pharisees had had a proper view of the need for spiritual healing (salvation), they would also have been able to develop a proper view of physical healing. Their negative response to His healing of a man with a crippled hand, however, was testimony to their spiritual hardness. The Pharisees hated Jesus all the more for what

He did on the Sabbath. As they saw it, showing mercy by healing when done on the Sabbath was horrible, but plotting to kill Jesus, the Healer, on the same day was a worthy act.

- Mark 5:24–34: Jesus encountered a woman with unremitting vaginal bleeding. She had been unsuccessfully treated, and spent all her savings seeking medical care. She sought Jesus as a physical healer, but she found that Christ (the Messiah) saves people such as her inwardly *and* outwardly. Jesus healed physically, but now she could view (and deal with) physical sickness differently in the future. Because of her condition and experience with failed treatments, she was fearful, helpless, and almost hopeless. After her encounter with Jesus, who told her to go in peace (verse 34), she had experienced a double blessing. Shalom (peace) refers to well-being in both the inner and outer man. Seeing and tasting the goodness of God in the physical realm would prepare her for responding properly to other hard times that God providentially brings into a person's life. We as Christian doctors also need to offer God's shalom. More specifics addressing this important topic are forthcoming.

- Matthew 8:16–17; Isaiah 53:4; Psalm 103:3; 1 Peter 2:24: Some have interpreted these verses as teaching the redemptive right of physical healing this side of heaven and via faith.[14] However, not all believers are physically healed in this life (although all are healed spiritually), and many unbelievers are healed physically. God did not promise to remove the effects of the curse of sin from the body in this life. Scripture draws a parallel: physical healing may or may not come in this life, but spiritual healing—a changed heart—always comes to those who believe (believing is a result of the changed heart).

When Jesus addressed the whole person, He did so outwardly and inwardly. He did not withhold that which would truly benefit struggling people for whom He had no medicine or medical procedures. Yet He helped people from the inside out. The internal dimension, however, always has a salutary effect upon the external. If you had medicine that you knew the patient needed, but you would not give it, what kind of medicine would you be practicing? If, as we have said, neu-

14   When Jesus healed a sick person, He did not take upon Himself that individual's condition, and He did not lift the curse of sin such that no sickness or misery is present in this life. Rather, "taking on the infirmities" means at least two things: Jesus took on man's infirmities by His deep and personal compassion *and* by His substitutionary suffering and sacrifice. He so identified with mankind that He understood what it meant to be fully human, yet He was without sin (Hebrews 4:15). Since healing comes to some unbelievers and not to all believers, the issue is not how much faith a person has in whether his body is healed on this earth or not. Rather, the issue is the expression of the simple faith of the believer.

trality is impossible, it follows that withholding God's truth from your patient is every bit as harmful. Biblical truth is like that medicine. Should it be withheld if it is appropriate for him in his situation and rightly ministered? Presenting to your patients biblical truth that will govern all of their lives is the ultimate expression of following Christ as a Christian physician. It will also greatly affect his view of medicine itself.

As a caveat, let's not forget that ten lepers were healed outwardly in Luke 17:11-19. Each one was truly healed physically and in the fullest meaning of the term. But only one—a Samaritan—was healed inwardly. He alone gratefully returned to Jesus praising God (17:16). Jesus' question in verse 17 is both a warning and a lament: Jesus asked, "Were not all ten cleansed? Where are the other nine?" Not all patients to whom you minister truth in God's name for His glory and the benefit of the patient will accept it. Perhaps most won't. Don't expect better results than the "Great Physician."

From this brief look at Jesus as the Great Physician, we see alongside of His many physical healings that the spiritual dimension of His ministry stands out loud and clear. Therefore, it would seem that, to practice medicine as a Christian, your approach to patients must be vertically as well as horizontally-oriented. Indeed, the vertical reference must be first since as a clinician, acting as such, it orients *your* thinking and work.

A proper vertical reference, at least in part, means that what you do and think, and what advice and how you give it, will be done for the glory of God (1 Corinthians 10:31; Colossians 3:17). That is one expression of thinking God's thoughts after Him. As a result, in humble submission to Christ, you will develop a mindset that considers the body a gift from God. Your concern in treating the patient will not only be for him, but, *more importantly*, to please God. Helping a patient to develop a proper vertical reference must be kept in view in all that you do in your practice. You might ask: how can I help the patient focus inwardly and vertically given my schedule and the patient's willingness (or unwillingness) to do so? I present examples along the way that focus on practical how-tos throughout this book. For now, remember that the principle of verticality and your commitment to it should not vary, although your application of it will vary depending on your comfort in presenting biblical truth to a particular patient and on the patient's receptivity and maturity as a Christian. And your "comfort" may be an index of your knowledge (both doctrinal and practical) of your faith!

In considering the effects of vertical thinking remember the following:

- All of life is theological, and you and the patient are theologians. Both need to become aware of this and realize that you both are engaged in theological activity.
- All believers, physicians and patients, are called to be

good theologians. Theological considerations must not be speculative but must always be a search for truth (Acts 17:11; Colossians 2:8). Our call is to be Bereans.

- As a physician, you are called to be a biblical-theological practitioner. That means you must study theology and determine its relevance for medicine.

- Good theology requires the theologian to function as a God-pleaser by becoming more like Christ (2 Corinthians 5:9; Romans 8:28-29: see footnote 22). It is more than simply getting doctrine straight.

- Using irritations that God has designed for patients to become "pearls"—one of the greatest blessings and privileges this side of heaven—must be kept in mind at all times. I have and will continue to highlight this too often neglected and easily ignored truth (see footnote 21). The pearl for the Christian is Christlikeness. The believer models Christ who chose to do what He did: leave heaven and come to earth as the God-man to live a perfect life and die a perfect death in order to please a perfect Father (John 4:31-34).

The desire to represent Christ with a Christlike demeanor should be a great desire for all Christians but especially for the practicing physician. Again, we need to define terms. Most Christian doctors seem to seek to model Christ's compassionate care. Apparently, this is a "given." *Yet,* I pondered even

that idea. As I have said earlier, some non-believing physicians
are nice, and (seemingly), may act even more morally correct
than some Christian physicians. The Gospels help us here by
teaching that Jesus was more than a Good Example, a Moral
Teacher *par excellence*, and a man who did not "make waves."
Fully addressing this issue moves us further into the area of
Christology: Who was Christ, what did He do, and what is
your view of what He did? Moreover, exactly how should
the doctrine of Christ and your relationship to Him affect
your practice?

We will continue to cover this subject in greater depth later,
but, for now, consider briefly what the Bible says about this
aspect of Christ's person and work:

- He is the Son of God (Matthew 4:3; 14:33; 16:16;
  27:54).
- He is the Son of Man (Daniel 7:13-14; Matthew 8:20;
  16:27; Mark 8:29-31).
- He is the Lord of lords and the King of kings (1 Timo-
  thy 6:15-16).
- He is a Friend of sinners (Matthew 11:19).
- He lived as the Servant King, and He died on the cross
  as the sacrificial Substitute for sinners otherwise des-
  tined to hell (Matthew 20:20-28; 2 Corinthians 5:21;
  Galatians 3:10-13; 1 Peter 1:18-19; 2:19-24).
- He is the true Peacemaker, but also the true Division-

Maker (Matthew 5:9; 10:32-38; John 14:27-29).

Faithfully and boldly representing Christ is a theological endeavor of top priority for Christian physicians. So it must be rightly understood. As Jesus healed the body, so too must the physician who is Christian. As Jesus brought about spiritual healing, so too must the physician who is a Christian. When he functions as an instrument in His Savior's hand to minister, this makes all the difference to your patient (positively or negatively). So how do these biblical truths about Jesus Christ affect medical practice? Our continuing question resurfaces: why write a book on being Christian in your medical practice? I am glad that you have read this far. There is more to come, including answers to all the questions that I have raised, but not answered, along the way.

In preparation for writing the book, I reviewed several historical writings and publications that address the *history* of medicine and its practice.[15] I examined the roots and origins

---

15   Multiple resources were used in gathering the information including the very helpful short volume: *A Short History of Medicine*, EH Ackerknecht, 1982, John Hopkins University Press; *Ancient Medicine Selected Papers* by Ludwig Edelstein ed: O Temkin and C: Temkin The John Hopkins Press Baltimore 1967; Encyclopedia of Medical History RE McGraw, 1985; McGraw-Hill Book Company, NY, NY; *The World Book Encyclopedia*, vol. 13, World Book Inc, 1986; www.greekmedicine.net; www.mdhealthnetwork. org; www.pbs.org/wgbh/nova/doctors/oath

of medicine and noted its development. One of my goals was to understand our heritage and its legacy in relation to my concerns. I was interested in determining the presence and the extent of Christian and other influences on medicine. The study was cursory but quite interesting and, at the same time, disturbing. Bear with me for a time as we skim over some of what I discovered.

Ancient Greek medicine (500 B.C. to 500 A.D.) is incomparably closer to modern medicine than any other historical form. It was also the brand of medicine practiced by doctors in the early church age. As was typical for others, Greece was a polytheistic society, and Apollo was considered the god of healing. About 475 B.C., he was replaced by Asclepius, who had a semi-religious cultic following and actually used the temple for healing. The roots of modern medicine are in ancient Greece. Of decisive importance for the development of Greek medicine was the influence of philosophy. Apparently, many of the early physicians were greatly influenced by the philosophers. Yet the main developments in medicine were not due to philosophical speculation as might be assumed, but, surprisingly, to the practice of *clinical observation*.

During this time, disease and healing tended not to be regarded as a supernatural phenomenon as in earlier days and in other cultures. It was approached from a rational, naturalistic, and "scientific" point of view. No definite reason has been given to fully explain this "important and radical step" in the practice of Greek medicine. The following, however, are some thoughts about it. Greek society allowed for individualism and critical thought, especially among the upper class. Apparently physicians separated religion (obviously the religion was not Christianity) from the practice of medicine. Hippocrates (460-377 BC) is reported to be the father of medicine. Not much is known about his life. But we do know that he espoused a materialistic, as opposed to a supernatural, explanation of disease. And we learn that he treated an individual not as a disease alone, but as a "whole person." He believed that "nature" (*phubis*) had strong healing effects, and the physician was to assist "nature." He is reported to have had high ethical ideals and practices that would be an advance upon earlier Greek religion and its relation to medical practice.

This is truly interesting information. After my short review of the history of medicine, I asked myself several questions:

- What did I learn?
- How has my thinking and practice of medicine been affected by what I learned?

I must say that it is disturbing to trace the history of medicine to its sheer pagan roots and then to realize what consequent effects it has had upon my training and practice. In my study, one fact stood out. Medicine has been steeped in anti-biblical thinking. The trend of Greek practice carries over into the medical literature of today. It is in this sense that medicine has not changed. Knowingly or unknowingly, God is attacked as the Creator of the universe and man as His creature. Sin has no place in medical training, especially in the fields of psychiatry and psychology (one wonders if you should consider these two as medical or more theological - philosophical). Ignored are the origin of sin and the effects of God's curse on sinners. Aging, for instance, is considered a natural process; efforts to slow it down or stamp it out are ubiquitous. Disease and misery are considered simply a part of life in the evolutionary process. The mystical, supernaturalistic beliefs that once influenced man's thinking and medicine in earlier times were replaced with the rationalism and empiricism that characterizes modern "scientific" medicine. This science is based on Greek-like empiric observation, thus making science the standard for every observation and interpretation of man and his infirmities. Often, this approach goes under the banner of evidence-based medicine.[16]

Science has been allowed to do the thinking for the doctor. Based on these observations, cause and effect is assumed for symptoms—even if the factual data don't support the conclusion. Theories are then developed, and when theories exist without factual data, the disjunction between science and religion is blurred. When this occurs, philosophy becomes, or at

16   See footnote 10

least functions, as theology. The post-modern existential view that is currently prominent in our culture further blurs the distinction between science and philosophy because personal subjectivity (feelings and experience) is the authority.

You might be wondering why I didn't gather more information using another or different questionnaire. I decided not to do on a larger scale what I had done on a smaller one. The information from the questionnaire was helpful and stimulating but certainly not unexpected. I suspect that on a larger scale I would find much more of the same. It did, however, encourage me to pursue the writing of this book. But I realized that this book could not be like any other. It had to contribute something more that was truly new and correct. Otherwise, you might not continue reading! I have become all the more interested in determining what God in His Word says about life as it pertains to the teaching and practice of medicine. As I have thought, prayed, and studied, for my own practice, lingering issues remained. Here are a few:

- Is there a way to be Christian in my/your medical practice that is untapped?
- Is there such a thing as the practice of biblically-based medicine?
- Is something more needed in the practice of medicine today and in decades to come that Christians must become aware of and implement?

- What legacy do I want to leave to younger physicians, and—more to the point—what legacy most honors God?

- How have we, as Christian physicians, helped prepare the church to guide physicians and patients in what should be a joint venture between physician and patient to become God's kind of doctor and patient?

- Are we fulfilling God's expectations of us as doctors in the practice of medicine?

In the milieu I have just described, the Bible will be our major reference book. That means much modern medical thought/therapy will be contrasted with it and challenged by it. My hope is that the writings of others will complement and extend what has been presented here.

CHAPTER 3

Your Approach to Medicine

THINK ABOUT YOUR FUNDAMENTAL AP-
PROACH to the practice of medicine. Is it any different
from how you approach all of life? Should it be? Are not the
two approaches interwoven into the very fabric of being a
new creature in Christ, a person regenerated by the Holy
Spirit (2 Corinthians 5:17 and John 3:3-8)?[17]

---

17 2 Corinthians 5:17: "Therefore, if anyone is in Christ, he is a new creation; the old has gone and the new has come!" John 3:3-8: "In reply Jesus
declared: I tell you the truth, no one can enter the kingdom of God unless
he is born again. "How can a man be born when he is old?" Nicodemus
asked. "Surely he cannot enter a second time into his mother's womb to be
born!" Jesus answered, "I tell you the truth, no one can enter the kingdom
of God unless he is born of water and the Spirit. Flesh gives birth to flesh,
but the Spirit gives birth to spirit. You should not be surprised at my saying,
'You must be born again.' The wind blows wherever it pleases. You hear its
sound, but you cannot tell where it comes from or where it is going. So it is
with everyone born of the Spirit."

The believer is a "new creation" as the result of the work of the Holy Spirit. This new creation is the result of a radical, supernatural event by which you have been transferred from Satan's kingdom of darkness and placed into God's kingdom of light. Your past fundamental self-focus has been replaced by a God-focus so that you are able to think, desire, and act as one of God's children. Consequently, you, as a Christian physician, have had your life turned upside down (or better, right side up), including the way that you think about and practice medicine. If you don't recognize the difference, then ask yourself why. Even if you are not experiencing the change in obvious ways in your practice, the fact of it should be uppermost in your mind. The "why" and "how" of this will become clearer as we move forward. Suffice it say now that your skill as a physician and the physical healing that you are to accomplish need never be in your own strength, without a proper vertical reference. You need that holy reference able to properly relate to your patient.

As a believer who is a physician, three facts should stand out.

- You have more to offer any patient, believer or unbeliever, than your unbelieving colleague.
- You are (or you are not) doing so.
- God has great expectations of you as a believing physician; He has given you His Holy Spirit and the Bible

to direct what you do.

I intend to help unpack these facts by delineating what "the more to offer" and what God's expectations of you are, as well as how you can begin to implement them in your daily practice. My present goal, however, is to present a perspective on medicine, doctors, and patients that, when you do understand and begin to implement, will change your practice of medicine for good.

Before unpacking the "something more" and God's expectations of you, let's examine some of the more obvious differences between believing and unbelieving physicians. If you have more to offer, and you do, that "more" must be related to what God has done (and will do) in your life and the life of your patient—especially when the patient is a believer.

Worldview

One major difference between you, a Christian physician, and the unbelieving physician to which I alluded earlier is your *worldview*. Scripture sets forth a radically different mindset, perspective, and approach to all of life—not just to the practice of medicine. You know that this is God's world and that He is active in it. That means He is active in *you* and in *your patient*. Can you rightly go to the office every day without recognizing this and how it will change your practice? Briefly, your worldview is a belief that the self-sufficient, self-contained, all-powerful, independent living God has ordained all that comes to pass for His glory and the benefit of His people. It has to do with the fact that some day you will live in God's presence. It has to do with the fact that He has given you a Book with answers to life's questions and directions about how to live. It also gives you an overall perspective on life that maybe summed up in these two verses:

> *And we know that in all things God works for the good of those who love him and have been called according to his purpose. For those God foreknew, he also predestined to be conformed to the likeness of His Son that he might be the firstborn among many brothers.*

> (Romans 8:28-29)

Here, Paul teaches that God is in charge and directs His world for His glory and the believer's benefit. Therefore, He is in the problem, up to something, and up to something good for the believer now *and* eternally. He even defines the basic good: conformity to Christ in thought, desire, and deed. Accordingly, you believe that He can be known properly by every believer, and is known improperly by the unbeliever. Moreover, this Creator-God is in intimate relationship with His creation, powerfully preserving, governing, and sustaining all of His creatures and all of their actions.[18] No fact or event occurs by chance or accident. The issue of control is settled. This vertical reference to God and life (when your response to God's saving you is proper) should correctly guide you in your relationship to others and to God's creation (your horizontal reference to life). This means that when acting, thinking, and desiring as a Christian should, the vertical controls the horizontal: you will always see problems through the lens of God's good, sovereign providence and His Word. And as a corollary, a proper vertical orientation controls thinking, wanting, and doing. That perspective, when operative in the office, in itself ought to be both a blessing and an encouragement to you and your patient. And your Christian worldview will carry over to your relationship to office personnel. They too will be blessed by the way you view and practice medicine.

God-dependent creatures who are saved are capable of

18   Theologians call part of God's controls His *providence*. God works all things after the counsel of His own will (Ephesians 1:11). What occurs in His world comes from His sovereign will and His power and direction to bring it about. There is a reason for everything – His reason and His purpose. God plans His work and works His plan using man's free choices to get what He decreed accomplished in time and space. Therefore, the twin issues of control and purpose/meaning in life has been settled in God's favor. Man answers to God and not the other way around. God is the ultimate reference point for life. There is no fact and no person that is not in some relationship to God; all are theologians. We must begin with Him.

functioning as good theologians by correctly viewing matters
in the light of God's Word (Psalm 36:9). Simply put, God has
concern for *and* answers to both you and your patient's questions. That the ever-present God is your environment is, probably, an unknown concept to your patient. God is omnipotent
(all powerful and His control is good) and He is omnipresent
(the world is His, and His presence is around us and in us as
His image bearers). God is man's environment (Psalm 139).
There is no escaping God.

Let us pause a moment and consider what kind of God
we are speaking about. In one sense, He is a most objection-
able kind of God. By that I mean He makes prodigious claims
about Himself. He is the great I Am: the self-sufficient, wise,
good, loving, merciful God who created the heavens and
the earth and saved His people. He humbles the proud but
lifts up the burdened and oppressed. Being the God that He
is, He rightly makes demands on His creatures. As covenant
Lord, He demands loyalty and allegiance. Again we find that
neutrality in life and the practice of medicine is a myth. God
wants to affect all of you.

No matter how a believer might think or feel, God is "his
rock and fortress, an ever-present help in time of trouble"
(Psalm 18:1-3; 46:1). Do you and your patient turn to God as
such, or do you attempt to find refuge elsewhere? How will
that seeking demonstrate itself? In eternity past, you were de-

signed to function as a physician in proper relationship to God (Ephesians 1:4: "For he chose us in him before the creation of the world to be holy and blameless in his sight"). The degree to which you recognize this and are in proper relationship to Him in thought, desire, and action is the degree to which you honor Him in and out of the office.

In summary, every fact and event, ranging from getting up in the morning (even if you had been on call) to seeing patients in the office, is related to God. Therefore, the issue of control *and* the meaning and purpose in life is settled: you are His, and He is yours. Specifically, God has ordained you to practice medicine. The question is how. Being God's kind of physician (becoming more like Christ as a physician) in order to help patients function as God's kind of patients is your *operative goal*. There is no higher calling for you as a Christian physician. As we progress, we will discuss how this ministry may take place.

Scripture

A second difference is your source of authority. Scripture is the basis for your worldview. Everyone has a standard, an authority that directs his or her life. Since that is the case, the only issue is "which one?" Is it yourself? Is it books? Is it medical authorities? The issue raises several fundamental points which lead to certain presuppositions:

- Man is because God is – his being is derivative and dependent on God.

- God is a self-revealing God. He speaks to His people primarily in His Word.

- Man, as an ethically and morally responsible being, is a knower. He was created as a revelation receiver, interpreter, and implementer.

- In the Garden, the issue for Adam and Eve was *not* in knowing; they already knew God, who spoke to them audibly (Genesis 2-3). They were able to view the whole of creation in the light of what God said. Their task was covenantal loyalty shown by obedience.

- The issue for believers today is not in knowing but how one knows and by what standard. And what does one do in response to that knowing? A controlling thought for every believer must be that apart from God's explanation of life (biblical truth), life simply doesn't make sense. The issue of standard is critical and has a direct bearing on the possibility of neutrality (discussed on pages 6-7, 10-11, 18, 23, 29). Those who promote neutrality assume that a person unaided by God's Word can arrive at a proper understanding of life—including how to care for the body. And when God is omitted from any discussion regarding health and disease, the patient is neither encouraged nor enabled to pursue the practice of biblical principles in relation to his illness or infirmity.

This is another example of the link between vertical and horizontal orientations.

While the Bible is *not* a medical textbook or a textbook on the treatment of physical problems, it does deal with everything that a believer needs for life and godliness, including one's part in the treatment of illness and the maintenance of health (2 Timothy 2:15-17, 2 Peter 1:3-4).[19]

What is "everything for life"? Peter is speaking of that which is necessary to live properly oriented to God. It includes the new birth, a changed heart, and the indwelling Holy Spirit. Here specifically, it is God's Owner's Manual for life, His Word in which He gives basic (and often specific) knowledge that will enable the believer to have a proper vertical orientation. The believer has exactly what he needs to properly address and respond to physical problems.

---

19   See pages 10 and 17 for a discussion of these passages: 2 Timothy 3:15-17: and how from infancy you have known the Holy Scriptures which are able to make you wise for salvation through faith in Christ Jesus. All Scripture is God-breathed and is useful for teaching, rebuking, correcting, and training in righteousness, so that the man of God may be thoroughly equipped for every good work. 2 Peter 1:3-4: His divine power has given us everything we need for life and godliness through our knowledge of him who called us by his own glory and goodness. Through these he has given us his very great and precious promises so that through them you may participate in the divine nature and escape the corruption of the world caused by evil desires. *These passages tell you how to be wise.*

You may be wondering how that can be. Your wondering brings us back to a pivotal issue: what is the goal of the practice of medicine? If you function as a body mechanic, the Bible will be of little use in your practice except to encourage you to function as a nice and caring person. If, on the other hand, you realize that life is a theological matter, then you will want to mine the treasures in God's Word for all it offers regarding other means of practicing medicine (Proverbs 2:1-10).

Consider that the culture's call for lifestyle changes (in order to improve health or to stay healthy) is simply borrowing from God's truth. God formed and designed the body to be cared for His way. Both you and your patient, if he is a believer, have a new Boss (Romans 10:9; Acts 16:31). You won't simply "tell" or encourage your patient to eat less and exercise more, nor would you simply say "pray about it." Depending on the patient, his problem, and your relationship with him, you want to strongly urge (not force) him to think and act as a good steward-theologian. For instance, his involvement in treating his blood pressure or managing his diabetes won't simply be a ritual of taking medications in order to prevent adverse consequences and to feel better. Rather, taking medicine will be an act of joyful thanksgiving for what God is doing for him through the provision of medications. This simple kindness of God should help him to remember the broken body of Christ on the cross and encourage him to rely on God's grace to function as God's kind of patient.

The best thing that any patient—or any person, really—can do for his health is to apply the Word of God to his life (Matthew 7:21-28). The writer of Proverbs put it this way:

> *Trust in the Lord with all your heart and lean not on your own understanding; in all your ways acknowledge him, and he will make your paths straight. Do not be wise in your own eyes, fear the Lord and shun evil. This will bring health to your body and nourishment to your bones.*
>
> (Proverbs 3:5-8)

In these verses, the contrast is between being wise (trusting and fearing the Lord) and being self-reliant, which is living by the culture's idea of truth. Scripture is God's means of supplying vital information through the Holy Spirit for the believer to help him make decisions that honor God and are good for his body (2 Timothy 3:15-17; 2 Peter 1:3-4). We shall come to a more concrete understanding of this in time. For now, try to digest the big picture. In essence, it is this: you practice medicine in a Christian manner when you are working side by side with your divine Colleague, who willingly supplies direction for you.

As a physician, you are accustomed to seeking an expert opinion in the form of another colleague, a reference book, or some thought leader. As a believer, you have ready access to the *only* final perspective on life—God's. God has more to say about life, medicine, and the body than most people think. Probably more than you think. And what God says in His Word is true, authoritative, and beneficial. In the book that you hold in your hands, we will explore just about all that God, the Designer of the physical body, has to say directly in Scripture about health and disease. Certainly, the One who designed your body and redeemed you by hanging on the cross for your sins has fundamental directions for how to use and take care of your body! Why would you expect anything less?

Man (Anthropology)

A third difference is your view of *man*. God is Creator, and man is His creature. "Simple enough," you say. However, as a result of Adam's sin and man's representative relationship to him, all mankind sinned when Adam sinned (Romans 5:12-14). The clarity of the Creator-creature distinction was blurred. As a result of sin's destructive powers, physical problems and misery entered into the world. These problems range from interpersonal troubles, to disease, aging, and death. If there were no sin, there would be no sickness and no need for the practice of medicine. There will be no need for physicians in heaven! (Revelation 21:1-4).

Your task in life, therefore, is directly related to Adam's sin.

Think seriously about that. *Every* true illness should remind you—and your patient—of the curse of sin. But it should also remind you of the truly good news—the Cross, salvation in Christ, with its salutary effects on the body. Thinking that way will help you become more and more God's kind of physician and your Christian patients God's kind of patients. Don't simply pass over that last thought. A good theologian-physician will think through the implication and make a proper adjustment in his practice of medicine. Both you and your patient must learn to honor God by recognizing *His* role in sickness. As you do, you will grow in Christlikeness, being satisfied that the illness can be a means of grace to believers. It is good to remind yourself of the non-negotiable truth: growing to become like Christ is the greatest privilege on earth for the believer (Ephesians 1:4; Romans 8:28-29; 2 Corinthians 5:9).

Further, since Scripture teaches that man is inner man and outer man—a duplex creature, as we saw—he *has* a material body, but he is *not* only body. He also has an inner spiritual life and a soul, and he lives out of his heart (see pages 16-17). These human aspects, especially his inner-man activities, bear upon his body and how he treats it. Man's duplexity means that the inner man and its activity (thinking, reasoning, purposing, doubting, trusting, and deciding) affects the outer man (and the other way around). These facts mean that you do what you do and feel what you feel because you think what you think and want what you want.

In summary, a proper knowledge of man as God's image bearer, who is dependent on God for all that is good, is essential in order for you to care for patients God's way. The application of this knowledge grows out of your commitment to Christ to be God's kind of physician.

Sin (Hamartiology)

A fourth difference between you and the non-Christian physician is your view of sin, which is something that he never considers. Sadly, sin as it affects the health of believers is something that only a few *Christian* physicians consider. God's standards, including moral absolutes were imbedded in all men at creation. Those moral absolutes deal with sin's effect on the body, in principle cover all bodily matters, and must not be neglected.

The concept of sin in our culture is almost non-existent. Yet, sinful rebellion against a holy and just God is the reason for sickness (1 John 3:4; 5:17). Sin is an ethical issue and a moral rebellion, and it always has both a vertical and horizontal dimension. Every sin against some other person is a sin against God as well. Every sin against God affects human beings. Sin is, therefore, directly related to medicine; no sin, no doctors.

Believers have physical problems—no one outruns the

curse of sin in his or her lifetime. All bodies are failing, some to a greater degree than others. But the believer also has all the tools to live vertically and thereby be victorious over sin and its bodily effects, *right now*. He doesn't have to wait until heaven. Eager to be a good steward of his health, he may go to the physician to honor God, with hope that his Christian doctor will help him do so. You will rejoice with patients who exhibit that approach to your care, especially when you are able to help them attain it.

In fact, God, in His providence, brings about physical problems in particular persons for any number of reasons, with or without a direct parallel between a patient's personal sin and his condition. For instance:

- The body cursed by God due to Adam's sin deteriorates; it "ages" as a result of the curse (2 Corinthians 4:16–18).

- The body may be affected by a specific disease or result from something done to the body by the patient or another person.

- Disease, or at least symptoms, may be the result of the patient's response to God's providence.

- Symptoms develop because the human body as a result of God's curse is flawed and will never be symptom-free this side of heaven.

- Because of the limitation of man's knowledge and technology, the medical world will always face the stark reality that more symptoms exist than causes for them.

- Symptoms may result from unbiblical responses by the patient because of his sinful desires and attitudes. Sin has consequences in varying degrees for everyone, even for believers.

- Symptoms and signs may result from actual tissue damage (disease) which produces abnormal organ function. These are the result of Adam's sin and God's curse.

Man rebels against God through commission (doing what is prohibited by God: 1 John 3:4; Romans 14:23) and through *omission* (failing to do what God commands - James 4:17). Today, people seem unaware of the fact that life is a moral drama played out daily from "the inside out"—from the heart. simultaneously functioning with a vertical and horizontal reference. Inner-man activities such as thoughts, plans, beliefs, choices, feelings, and desires are expressed outwardly in word, thought, and deed (Matthew 15:18; Mark 7:20-21). Therefore, God commands His people to guard their hearts (Proverbs 4:23). Expressions of the heart either please God (demonstrated as a love for *and* obedience to God's Word) or please self (doing what you want for your reasons). The path of loving obedience is the path of the wise, and the path of arrogant disobedience is the path of the fool (Proverbs 4:18-19). The latter is characterized by discontentment, dissatisfaction, and unpleasantness—in short, hardness of life (Proverbs 3:5-8; 13:15). Proverbs 3:5-8 teaches that fear of the Lord, wisdom, and good health are linked positively, while trusting self, foolishness, and poor health are linked negatively. It will be one way or the other; remember, no neutrality!

The believing physician and only he, as we've seen, is able to minister to the whole person as God wills. Man is not only body. His inner man affects the outer man and *vice versa.* Sin's effects are in us and all around us—and can be detected especially in the doctor's office! The wise Christian physician will address the whole person, not only looking for sin but rather focusing on that which is truly good news: God has solutions for hurting people and hurting bodies.

In summary, only the believing physician understands that the body has been affected by sin and God's curse. Every person was stillborn spiritually (separated from God) and will die physically (separation of body and soul). **The fact that death, sickness, and misery are the direct result of the curse needs to be personalized.** If there is a direct relation between a person's physical problems and sin, and there may be, it may not be obvious to the person or the physician. Part of the obligation of the Christian physician is to help his patient realize that repentance, not necessarily medication or surgery, is the key to whole-person care.[20]

The Physical Body

There is a fifth difference: your view of the body. Everyone is a steward-theologian by virtue of God's creational design. Wrong thinking about God, self, and one's body leads to wrong thinking and actions about all of life, including how one takes care of his body. The believer is responsible for taking care of his body God's way *and* using it for God's glory. Remember what God tells you in Proverbs 3:7-8 ("Do not be wise in your own eyes, fear the Lord and shun evil. This will bring health to your body and nourishment to your bones"). A good steward considers himself indebted to God for his redemption. Heeding this admonition to live healthfully is what good stewardship is all about.

Stewardship involves God-given responsibility *with accountability*. It involves taking care of the body (remember: in God's providence, his body has been entrusted to him), regardless of whether it is failing or not. The Christian physician consciously talks to his patient about these matters and helps him

20   The all-important topic of repentance is addressed later in the book. Repentance is about change – in thinking that results in fruits. The Greek word *metanoia,* used to translate repentance, means a "turned around mind" – a different way of thinking about God, self, and his actions or inactions. Also see footnotes 31 and 51, pages 57 and 130.

with becoming a good theologian-steward. He does that by focusing on the real issue: it is not the body only but how he takes care of it. The believer will have to give an account of the care he gives the body (see Luke 16:1-13; 19:11-27; Matthew 25:14-30). He is bought with a price, and his body belongs to God by redemption as well as by creation. The Christian physician must also demonstrate good stewardship to his patients in how he handles his own body. When the physician functions in this manner, it is a win-win situation: God is glorified, the patient benefits, and the physician knows that he has pleased God.

The body that anyone has is the only one he will get in this life. God has shown enough concern for it that He has given written instructions that deal with its care. Consider Paul's words:

> *All sorts of things are lawful for me, but everything isn't advantageous. All sorts of things are lawful for me, but I won't be ruled by any of them. "Food is for the stomach and the stomach is for food" — true, but God will destroy both of them. But the body is not for sexual immorality but for the Lord and the Lord is for the body — but God raised the Lord and will raise us through His power. Don't you know that bodies are members of Christ? Shall I therefore take the members of Christ and make them members of a*

> *prostitute? Of course not! Don't you know that the*
> *one who is joined to a prostitute becomes one body*
> *with her? "Because," He says, "the two shall become*
> *one flesh." But the one who is joined to the Lord*
> *becomes one spirit with Him. Flee sexual sin. There*
> *are all sorts of sinful things that a person may do that*
> *are outside his body, but the one who commits sexual*
> *sin, sins against his own body. Don't you know that*
> *your body is a temple of the Holy Spirit who is in*
> *you, whom you have from God? You are not your*
> *own, since you were bought with a price; so glorify*
> *God in your body.*
>
> (1 Corinthians 6:12-20)

How many doctors and patients think of such truths when giving and receiving medical care? Paul taught that God designed the body and has something to say about how it is to be used and cared for. A person's body is not for self-pleasure. (In these verses the context is sexual immorality, but Paul's words have a much broader application. Self-pleasing is the modus operandi for all unbelievers, and too often for believers, in varying degrees and in a variety of ways.) His body is to be used in the service of the Lord. Good stewardship of the body is a vital way of serving the Lord, and serving the Lord is, therefore, good stewardship. In these verses, Paul spells out several truths regarding good stewardship:

- The body is the Lord's: verses 19-20.
- The Lord is *for* the believer's body: verse 14 – that is to say, He wants the best for it.
- The bodily resurrection of Christ and that promised to the believer is God's guarantee that God is for the body: verse 14. Therefore, the believer is also to be for the body God's way.
- The individual believer, body and soul, is part of the larger spiritual body (the church) of which Christ is Head: verse 15. What affects one, affects all members of the body.
- The believer is indwelt by the Holy Spirit: verse 19. We should keep healthy for His sake!
- The believer's body is not his; it is the Lord's and is to be used for glorifying Him: verse 20 (also see 1 Corinthians 7:23).

In essence, Paul taught that God has invested much in the believer for whom He paid an infinite price (v.20). The believer—both inner and outer man—is the Lord's. Therefore, the Christian has no other *logical* choice than to please God *with* his body (Romans 6:6; 12:1-2). The Christian physician has no logical choice other than to help his patient honor God with his body. These facts are not open for discussion. Good stewardship is a joint effort, usually *requiring* the physician to teach and exhort believers about biblical principles concerning healthful living and requiring the patient to apply those principles.

Sanctification and the Goal of Life

A sixth difference is your view of what daily life is all about. The believer is the most radically changed person on earth. Remember, he has had a radical heart operation and as a result is a new creation (Ezekiel 36:25-27; John 3:3-8; 2 Corinthians 5:17). Therefore, among other things, he has a new set of spectacles by which he views God, self, the universe, and life. As a result, his perspective of what he should know, desire, and do differs radically from that of the unbeliever. But his transformation did not end with regeneration. It only began. The believer ought to be a continually changing person.[21] How so? He has a new heart

---

21   There is growth after salvation. Theologians call this progressive sanctification. The believer, now with perfect standing and status in Christ, as God's child, never to be removed from that family, has work to do. Progressive sanctification is God's work of free grace whereby believers are renewed in the whole man after the likeness of Christ, and enabled to die more and more to sin and self-pleasure, and live more and more as one of God's children ought to. The believer was entirely passive in the work begun at salvation by the Holy Spirit (regeneration). The work the Holy Spirit is continuing to do through God's sanctifying grace enables the Christian to grow into Christlikeness (see Philippians 2:12-13). The concept of the

responsive to God, and he has the indwelling of the Holy Spirit. He should, then, have a positive growing relationship with God, manifested by thinking God's thoughts and following God's will. God's purpose for man is spelled out in 2 Corinthians 5:9 and Romans 8:28-29.[22]

Sanctification is the act of God's grace by which the believer dies to selfish ends by turning from a self-serving agenda and grows more and more into the new creature that he is becoming. He will be increasingly responsive to godly advice and biblical truth so that he can and will function as God's kind of patient. *That is fine for the patient but what's my role?* Glad you asked! Certainly, doing physical things to help the patient's physical problem is one key to being a Christian physician. But as we have seen, that is only the beginning. That key unlocks all of your patient's doors. Use it well. It should encourage and motivate you to function as a facilitator in helping the patient in his process

---

Christian oyster, discussed throughout the book, pictures this activity (see footnotes 22 and 26).

22   2 Corinthians 5:9: "So we make it our goal to please him, whether we are at home in the body or away from it." Romans 8:28-29: "And we know that know that in all things God works for the good of those who love him who have been called according to his purpose. For those God foreknew he also predestined to be conformed to the likeness of his Son that he might be the firstborn among many brothers."

of sanctification. That is a most worthy response of being a Christian physician.[23]

Ecclesiology (the doctrine of the Church)

A seventh difference is your view of the church. The church is God's chosen people who are called out and faithful to the end (Romans 1:6-7; 1 Corinthians 1:2; Revelation 17:14). It is the body of believers, and their seed, joined together as one body indwelt by the Holy Spirit with Christ as its Head (1 Corinthians 3:16; Eph 2:20). Christ exercises His Lordship over the church through His Word and Spirit. God has given ordained teaching and ruling officers as gifts to His church. By them the Church is able to fulfill the task of changing people's lives through the authoritative ministry of His Word (Ephesians 4:8-14; 2 Timothy 3:15-17). Since medical issues are potentially universal, some type of "medical ministry," as we are setting forth, should be a part of every church's teaching curriculum.

As the body of Christ, God's people "go about doing good,"

---

23   Romans 12:1-2: Therefore I urge you, brothers, in view of God's mercy to offer your bodies as living sacrifices, holy and pleasing to God – this is your spiritual act of worship. Do not be conformed any longer to the pattern of this world, but be transformed by the renewing of your minds. Then you will be able to test and approve what God's will is – his good, pleasing, and perfect will.

first to those in the household of faith, and second to those outside the church (Galatians 6:10; Matthew 5:14-16; John 13:34-35). They do this through biblical "one anothering."[24] One anothering is the call to help each other to mature into Christlikeness out of gratitude for the blessings of salvation. These activities include:

- Encouragement: Romans 15:4-5,13-14; 1 Thessalonians 5:11,12-14
- Exhortation: Romans 12:1; 1 Corinthians 1:10;4:14; Ephesians 4:1; Philippians 4:2
- Comforting: John 14/16; 2 Corinthians 1:3-4; 2:7; 1 Thessalonians 2:7-12; 3:7
- Stirring up: Hebrews 10:23-25
- Counseling: Romans 15:14; Colossians 3:16
- Forgiveness: Ephesians 4:31-32; Colossians 3:12-13; James 5:16
- Hospitality: 1 Peter 4:9-10
- Intimacy: Romans 16:16; 1 Corinthians 16:20; 2 Corinthians 13:12; 1 Peter 5:14

While the list of these activities is not exhaustive, the main message is that you as a Christian physician (and the patient as a believer or a potential one) have a storehouse of resources for helping hurting people. A Christian physician will make

---

24   For a more extensive study of this area, contact me (jimhalla@yahoo.com) for additional information.

himself aware of these resources and make regular use of them.
Later, we will discuss specific ways to use the benefits that
God has given to His people. But, for now, let it suffice to say
that every one of them has healing potential.

The Last Days (Eschatology)

An eighth difference is your view of man's ultimate destiny (eschatology). As a prelude, every person knows that it
is appointed for him to die (although he suppresses it). Then
comes judgment (Hebrews 9:27). Death is a reality for every
person unless he is alive at Jesus' return. And after death, all
people will stand before the judgment seat of God and Christ
to answer for, among other things, the use of he made of his
body (Romans 14:10,12; 2 Corinthians 5:10).[25] The reality
of judgment or the failure to properly consider God's judgment, often results in a wide variety of sinful and unhealthy
behaviors that are captured in the following Proverbs:

- Proverbs 1:19: Such is the end of all who go after ill-
  gotten gain; it takes away the lives of those who get it.
  (In contrast is Proverbs 28:16: A tyrannical ruler lacks
  judgment, but he who hates ill-gotten gain will enjoy

---

25   The word in the New Testament for judgment (*krino* and its de-
rivatives) indicates an upright, just evaluation by sorting out by the act of
separating. God separates the goats and the sheep. God is a discriminating
God so that all wrongs are made right (Matthew 25:31-46; 2 Thessalonians
1:5-10).

a long life.)

- Proverbs 5:21-23: For a man's ways are in full view of the Lord, and he examines all his paths. The evil deeds of a wicked man ensnare him; the cords of his sin hold him fast. He will die for lack of discipline, led astray by his own folly.

- Proverbs 10:24: What the wicked dreads will overtake him; what the righteous desire will be granted.

- Proverbs 10:27: The fear of the Lord adds length to life, but the years of the wicked are cut short.

- Proverbs 10:28: The prospect of the righteous is joy, but the hopes of the wicked come to nothing (see Proverbs 11:7, 23).

- Proverbs 28:1: The wicked flees when no one pursues but the righteous are as bold as a lion.

These selected verses indicate that every unbeliever has a fear of death and judgment. Even the atheist, though he bitterly denies and suppresses it, fears death. Such is the result of the fall and God's curse on mankind. Only the believer, because he is in Christ, has the capacity not to fear death since Christ has defeated the one who holds the power of death (Hebrews 2:14; 9:27; 1 Corinthians 15:54-57). Therefore, life may be, and *should* be, lived to the fullest, which means living the life that 2 Corinthians

5:9 prescribes.[26] Failure to do so may lead to various sort of illness or exacerbate existing ones.

The believer knows that this earthly life is not all there is and that he will face a God who will be reckoned with. Consequently, his worldview should be radically different from the unbeliever's. The unbeliever lives *for* and *by* the present (the "now," the temporal). He is motivated almost exclusively by what satisfies his senses and feelings. In contrast, the Christian knows that this earthly life is transitional. He knows that his citizenship, i.e., his permanent residence, is not here but heaven (Philippians 3:19-20). And that should make all the difference in how he cares for his body:

> *How great is the love the Father has lavished on us, that we should be called children of God! And that is what we are! The reason that the world does not know us is that it did know not him. Dear friends, now we are children of God, and what we will be has not yet been made known. But we know that when he*

---

26   See footnote 21-22 for discussion of this verse in regards to the meaning and purpose of life and becoming more like Christ. The 2 Corinthians 5:9 person is one who is becoming more and more like Christ, which is his only logical service to God (Romans 12:1-2).

appears, we shall see him as he is. Everyone who has
this hope in him purifies himself just as he is pure
(1 John 3:1-3).

John tells his readers that the real key to living is with an eternal perspective (v.2-3; see Colossians 3:1-3 for a similar emphasis by Paul). The prospect and promise of being in God's presence where there are no more tears, crying, or pain, when rightly understood, is an awesome, confident motivation for God's people. This eternal perspective enables one to persist in the maturing process of becoming more like Christ even *through* and *by* pain (Revelation 21:1-4; Hebrews 12:1-3; James 1:2:4, 12; see my book titled *Endurance* for more on that subject). Thinking vertically by viewing one's present condition through the lens of his future destiny, all the more, should enable a believer to become a good patient. This same perspective should significantly help you to function and grow as a Christian physician.

Another aspect of the doctrine of the Last Days is that of dying. Technology will not vanquish the curse of God for our sin or its effects. We die. A vast array of "grief counseling" theories and technologies are on the scene. They offer a full gamut of "treatment" options that include saying nothing, screaming, playing music, and almost anything in between (such as reading self-help books, "waiting it out," and medication.[27] Music therapy may even be a standby, apparently from the days of Saul).

How will you address your frail and dying patient? One article from the UK reported that a physician's self-proclamation of being religious (not necessarily Christian) or non-religious influences his or her ethics personally in terms of end-of-life decisions.[28] I would add that being "non-religious" (however defined) is a non-neutral bias and makes a moral statement to patients and other physicians. Will you abdicate your responsibility as a Christian physician and turn your patient and his care over to the culture, with its multifaceted views of "handling death and dying?" Or will you rely upon truth as given by the Creator, Designer, and Redeemer of the whole person? *God* is worthy of your efforts, and His people are entitled to His truth. Shouldn't God's Word be applied to this area of life since *all* of life is theological? The emphatically resounding answer is yes! Every Christian physician should clearly understand, and in his practice apply, the teachings of 1 Thessalonians 4 and 2 Corinthians 5. See appendix C for a discussion of these verses.

---

27   See my book on the subject, *Joy in Grief: God's Answer for Hard Times,* and pamphlet, *God's Wisdom for Troubled Times*

28   "Physician's Religious Beliefs Influence End-of-Life Decisions": BMJ-British Medical Journal (2010, August 26). "Doctors' religious beliefs strongly influence end-of-life decisions, study finds." *ScienceDaily*.

More to Offer

The last paragraph moves us into the concretely "more" elements that you have to offer. As a Christian physician, *you* have so much *more* to offer than your non-Christian colleague that I would take up the space of several books to cite, explicate, and illustrate. And there is a wealth of such books upon which you can draw for exegetical help. Consider only some of these "mores."

The first "more" is *truth* – God's truth. While all truth is God's truth, it is also *true* that all error is Satan's error. All truth helps; all error hurts. How do you decide which is which? What is your authority and standard for deciding? Jesus declared that He is the way, the truth, and the life (John 14:6). Pilate, in John 18:38, asked, "What is truth?" Ironically, the Truth—Jesus Christ—was standing before his very eyes, but Pilate, ignorant of truth, failed to acknowledge Him. For the believer, truth is always Jesus, the Living Word, and the Scripture, God's written Word, from which we learn about Him. Jesus, in John 17:17, prayed, "Sanctify them by the truth; your word is truth." Further, Paul informs us that believers have the mind of Christ by virtue of possessing His Holy Spirit who is the spirit of truth (John 16:13). Believers are called to live like it (1 Corinthians 2:16; Philippians 2:5). What a difference there ought to be between a physician who has truth and one who does not! Agreed?

Truth and sanctification (the process of growing daily more and more like Christ) are inextricably linked. The process of sanctification (see footnote 21) involves the twofold process of putting off and putting on (Ephesians 4:22-24; Colossians 3:8-10). The call of God to grow is through the Holy Spirit as the believer regularly and consistently replaces the former self-deception and Satan's lies that he used to live by with biblical truth. He should now be motivated by a desire to please God out of gratitude for the cross. The key concept is summarized by three words: truth, life, and ministry. How is your practice characterized by each of these? Truth guides life; it is *for* living a godly life. Life demonstrates how truth is applied. Ministry inevitably follows truth and life, including the way you view your work as a doctor.[29]

---

29   The Bible represents the link between truth and growth in Christlikeness in the following passages (not an exhaustive list!): Titus: 1:1: "Paul, a servant of God and an apostle of Jesus Christ for the faith of God's elect and the knowledge of the truth that leads to godliness,"; Psalm 119:9-11:24: " How can a young man keep his way pure? By living according to your word. I seek you with all my heart; do not let me stray from your commands. I have hidden the word of God in my heart so that I might not sin against you. Your statutes are my delight; they are my counselors; 1 Timothy 4:6-8: "If you point these things out to the brothers, you will be a good minister of Jesus Christ, brought up in the truths of the faith and of the good teaching that you have followed. Have nothing to do with godless myths and old wives tales; rather train yourself to be godly. For physical training is of some value, but

We have seen that people don't change in the abstract and don't live that way, either. Change occurs when falsehood is replaced with truth. Unlike all other supposed deities, our God is self-revealing. He powerfully reveals Himself in His Son, the created order, and His written Word, the Bible. And because Jesus is truth, truth is personal, absolute, and objective. Truth is not impersonal, abstract, relative, or subjective, as pundits of our culture would have us believe. While all truth is God's truth, don't forget that all error is Satan's error. It is of vital importance to learn how to distinguish between the two. That means a thorough, not superficial, study of the Scriptures. God reveals nothing through unbelievers, but some justify their errors by claiming that "they" were revealed to them. An unbeliever may be said to "discover" truth. But he is really only discovering facts that always point to the God of the Bible, though he denies that vertical reference. Unbelievers cannot reveal truth because they have no living and vital relationship with God, the Source of truth. If this fact doesn't impact your practice by demonstrating your contact with applicable truth, then your

---

godliness has value for all things holding promise for both the present life and the life to come. " Life and ministry are to be expressed in obedient living. Loving Christ is demonstrated by living according to biblical principles and helping others do the same (John 14:15, 21, 23,31). *If one has no truth, then there will be no obedient living. Such was the case with Pilate.*

practice must change.[30]

How do you decide whether something is true or false? Besides 2 Timothy 3:15-17 and 2 Peter 1:3-4, which we have discussed previously, Isaiah, in 8:20, answers that all-important question. "To the law and to the testimony! If they do not speak according to this word, they have no light of dawn."

God's word is truth, because it is His powerful, purposeful self-expression and vice versa. It is only by hearing and heeding God's word that there will be light and blessings for God's people. The same is true as well for you and your patient.

Consider several examples of applied truth that should be relevant to any practice. How does Psalm 36:9 ("In that light we see light") apply? The basic truth regarding man is that he is an image bearer of God and that man lives out of an identity. Yet so many patients put their identity in their health and its preservation or in their medical condition and the pursuit of relief. They express that fact by such terms as a cancer survivor, an arthritic, and even a caregiver. People live out of who they think they are (identity), which gives them an agenda for life, and its pursuit controls their lives. An inordinate desire to

---

30   There are consequences for each choice. Proverbs 13:15 ("Good understanding wins favor but the way of the unfaithful is hard"), for example, contrasts the way of the wise and the way of the fool. The way of the fool is the way of the unfaithful – the person who seeks his own interest using his own logic; he *can expect hardness* in this life as well as eternally.

be what they want rather than to be what God has designed is bondage and only leads to further bondage. As a result of their pursuit, your job as a physician is complicated, and their definition of freedom leads to a counterproductive pursuit of it. A proper understanding of life and God's design for each believer leads to good stewardship, not for relief necessarily (that may come as a byproduct) but to please God.

A second truth applicable to medical practice is the issue of sin and its source of origin—the heart. Sin complicates life, and affects the body. God's answer for sin is repentance and the fruit of repentance.[31] In medical practice, sin may show up in a patient's life in a number of ways: being sinned against and a sinful response, sinning against someone by holding grudges (which complicates the initial sin), or by practicing "unhealthy" (actually sinful) lifestyles, especially as the patient "handles life" (such as smoking, using drugs, over or under-eating, or lack of exercise to mention a few). The behavior is not the only or even major problem. The heart of the matter (excuse the pun) is the person's heart. Stopping the behavior is

---

31   Repeatedly, the necessity for a correct understanding and application of the doctrines of forgiveness and repentance is needed to help patients improve their medical condition or get victory in it. In the pages to come, I will give examples of this truth as applied to certain patients. Only the physician-theologian is able to bring this much-needed, proper biblical medical instruction.

one thing; unbelievers do that, and unbelieving physicians can help patients stop. The person's motivation for sinning against God and others is the critical issue. You, Christian physician, are in the blessed position to bring true deliverance through the gospel. God's grace through a changed heart is the gospel, which is the power and wisdom of God (Romans 1:16-17; 1 Corinthians 1:18, 21, 24). Repentance and forgiveness should be part of your arsenal in bringing true freedom to your patients.

Truth is power; it sets people free from the darkness, tyranny, and power of sin (John 8:31-36). Truth and freedom are inextricably linked to Jesus Christ. This means that a relationship with God is powerful; you might say it is dynamite ("I can do everything through him who gives me strength" Philippians 4:13).[32] Therefore, when hard times come into the lives of one of God's children, as a physician, you (possessing truth) can

---

32   The Greek word translated "give me strength" is *endunamoo.* Our English words *dynamic, dynamo,* and *dynamite* highlight the power that this word displays. See Romans 4:20, Ephesians 6:10, and 2 Timothy 2:1. Paul's "all things" is responding to life in a way that honors God. The meaning of the verse is not that anyone can do what he wants at God's expense. It does mean that the believer can do that which God delights in and requires of him as a growing believer. In this verse, "all things" refers to that which Paul called the Philippians to get busy doing: resolving the disunity problem (4:2-3) and "keeping on keeping on" as part of the sanctification process individually and corporately (1:27-2:13).

help steer him toward healthful, biblical priorities.

Consider this example. Faced with the unknown (such as what is going to happen to me in the face of my cancer, renal failure, or rheumatoid arthritis – RA) and the known (such as how will I survive the treatments, how will I make it, how will I meet my responsibilities as a spouse, parent, and person), what direction and guidance do you give your patient? Armed with the basic truths that the truth will set him free and that truth is power, you can offer him true hope. He can be God's kind of patient because he is a new creature in Christ who deserves to be honored (2 Corinthians 5:17). You must draw the connection between the person's situation and a Savior who blazed the trail of faithful living and now sits in His rightful place of preeminence interceding for him (Hebrews 4:15-15; 6:13-20; 12:1-3). This Savior not only provided Himself for your patient but also faithful believers such as yourself and the church family to encourage, to edify, to comfort, to challenge, and even to confront given the situation and the personal relationship of each party. God is very good!

As the example shows, in lieu of medications to help your patient handle life, the truth will set him (and you) free from much of the effects of illness *and* its treatment by making him (and you) you wise. Proverbs 1:7 and 9:10-12 say that the fear of the Lord is the beginning of knowledge. Fear of the Lord includes the dominating, reverent awareness that God is God and that He has something to say about your every thought, desire, and action. Fear of the Lord is a gift from God, because God is in the business of producing wise men (Psalm 1:1-3). Physicians, as well as patients, certainly need wisdom! They ignore it to everyone's disadvantage. Correctly bringing God into a person's thinking in any situation, especially a physical one, is a fundamental principle. As we have emphasized, it is essential for helping the believer to become a good theologian-steward and as a functioning Christian oyster (see footnotes 21-22, 26, 34).

Let's consider an example of a wise physician. What is your definition and how does it match up with God's? Wisdom is knowledge, but it is also skill in applying that knowledge. While the Bible is not a medical textbook, it is all a believer – physician *and* patient - needs to properly <u>respond</u> to physical problems. It is, I repeat, the believing Christian physician's *and* patient's *Owner's Manual.* So, when the Bible speaks about taking care of the body, it is authoritative. Let me reiterate some truths that the Bible teaches in regard to the body and the Christian's responsibility in its care and illustrate how the wise physician can use each of those truths in daily practice.

- God designed your body, saved it, and entrusted it to you (1 Corinthians 6:12-20). The patient is sitting across from you wondering, asking, even demanding, what is wrong with him. In times like this, he may not be a "happy camper." He may want to know if this is what life is all about. The wise physician knows that the patient's focus is purely physical. A proper vertical reference is missing. He knows that he must bring God into the picture. Armed with that mindset, he prays and looks for opportunities to do so.

- The Designer, who is also your Owner, has set forth ways for you to take of your body. The wise physician, thinking vertically, considers what biblical truth to bring to bear on the patient in his situation.

- As a result of God's ownership, you are obligated to care for your body as a good theologian-steward. As His child, you are privileged to do so. You gather information, not only on the problem from the patient's perspective, but from God's. Say the physical problem is one of coronary disease. The wise physician inquires about ways the patient has and hasn't been a good steward. Questions about "handling life" are included. The issue of "stress" will invariably enter the discussion. The wise physician knows that the problem is not "what is out there" but his patient's response to it. Helping the patient draw a relationship between a sinful response to life issues including his body problem, and symptoms that include worsening of his heart disease, enables the physician to gently but accurately bring God into the picture.

- Stewardship is a theological issue and a universal life principle. God expects an accounting. A steward is a person who has been entrusted with something that belongs to another in order to take care of it. The question for every believer is whether he will function as a good or bad theologian-steward. The wise physician knows that the principle of sowing and reaping has a bearing on his patient's health (Galatians 6:7). He may call to mind the biblical story of the ant and grasshopper that has been immortalized in older cartoons (Proverbs 6:6-11). If the patient continues to drink, to smoke, to get angry, and to sin against God and his body, he can expect unhealthy consequences. On the other hand, the wise physician knows that good stewardship has its own reward.

In summary, applying biblical principles to the whole person is the best thing a believer can do for his health, and it is one thing that wise physicians do (Proverbs 3:5-8). As I have said, two of God's priorities for the Christian physician are for him 1) to use his skill with finesse in regard to physical healing, and 2) to help the patient function as a theologian-steward who honors God. He does this by putting his theology to work.[33]

---

33   Titus 2:14: "who gave himself for us to redeem us from all wickedness and to purify for himself a people that are his own, eager to do what

The wise physician knows that the patient's general goal in coming to him for treatment is for relief. Your goal as a physician, and no matter the body problem, is not simply to bring him relief but also to help turn his focus to pleasing God in his problem. God may say "no" to relief or cure. However, relief may come as a byproduct, and for that, both you and he can be grateful.

The *operative principle* for you, as a physician, however, is to make it easy for your patient to function as a good theologian-steward, and hard not to function as one. In the end it is his choice, and many patients who are Christians choose not to function biblically. While you are not responsible for their choices, you are responsible for explaining how to be God's kind of patient and attempting to persuade him to be such. One vivid example from my own experience involved a woman with RA who was a smoker. Smoking and RA are not a good pair. In fact, evidence suggests that smoking hinders the salubrious affects of remittive-inducing agents. Moreover, an already inefficient body is rendered more inefficient because of an elevated carboxyhemoglobin level—with or without

---

is good." Paul paints God's larger purpose in salvation. It is to secure for Himself a peculiar people—a people all His own who honor Him by their lifestyles—attitudes and actions, beliefs and behavior. As a result of his salvation, the Christian will be eager to do what is good according to God's standard, motivated by faith and love, and for God's glory.

emphysema. The patient had physical problems beyond RA and—more importantly—after talking to her I knew that she had a far more serious problem. Her poor stewardship was a result of handling life sinfully. She said, "Don't talk to me about smoking. I smoke because it is the only friend I have and it helps me handle life." In this case, I opened the door as wide as I could for presenting biblical truth to her, and I left the results to the Lord.

Relief, however defined, may not come even with good stewardship. If relief doesn't come, pleasing God by becoming more like Christ as I have just demonstrated has its own rewards. Acquiring a satisfied and contented life with an increasing awareness of its eternal perspective is one of them. [34] *Using* the unpleasantness of hard times as a means of pleasing God is virtually unthought-of by patients *and* doctors. Yet it is a prime lesson of the cross. In fact, it is one of the greatest blessings and privileges that any believer has. Consider this

---

34   The concept of becoming more like Christ is a rich one, and I have discussed it in several places in the book (see footnotes 21-22, 26). In the area of the practice of medicine, it deserves further study. Paul speaks about it in both 2 Corinthians 5:9 ("So we make it our goal to please him, whether we are at home in the body or away from it") and Galatians 2:20 ("I have been crucified with Christ, and I no longer live, but Christ lives in me. The life I live in the body, I live by faith in the Son of God, who loved me and gave himself up for me").

example, again from the world of rheumatology.

A young married woman, the mother of two, told me about aches and pains, multiple diagnoses and multiple treatment regimens, and continued pain, fatigue, and—by her own words—a "poor" response to life. She was a believer but did not look forward to having "to put up" with her problems. Her problems included far more than her physical complaints. She wanted relief; it hadn't come, and now she was stuck. Or so she thought. In fact, she took to heart much of the reading material I give routinely to patients and also the pamphlet, "Christ and Your Problems," an abbreviated explanation of 1 Corinthians 10:13 designed to give hope. After several visits, paying attention to her and treating her physical complaints, and interacting with answers to the questions I had assigned, she said something to this effect: "my pain and fatigue may never go away, but that is OK. I can learn to trust God. I see when I try to do things in my own strength, my body lets me know. So instead of trying to get rid of my pain and fatigue, I use them to remind myself of God's goodness to me. I still hurt, but I am not devastated. My husband and family see the difference."

This woman was blessed, and I was blessed. God in His graciousness did not leave her or me. What an awesome display of his grace and mercy!

Here is another example of a patient using what she wishes

were not there (and doesn't like) to please God. A woman, who had a number of medical problems, compounded them by smoking. She had several reasons why she smoked and at the same time said that she had stopped and resumed smoking— again and again. She said she knew the smoking was for her: to make her feel better. Yet she was a believer and agreed "it" did not please God (more correctly, she was not pleasing God). She said that she knew smoking was bad for her health. However, my goal was not for her to stop smoking but to honor God. She wanted to know how she could do that. She was not willing to leave off the last five cigarettes. When asked why, she replied that the pain was too much; she didn't want to go through the "withdrawal." That set in motion the application of the biblical principle of "gain through loss" and using what is unpleasant for victory. I asked the patient to *use* the potential for pain for good. Instead of avoiding the pain and discomfort as a reason to continue to dishonor God, every time she thought of her pain, she was to remind herself of the cross which declared to her and to the world that her God is big, and He is good.

She was aware of this type of thinking. She remembered her pregnancies and recalled the gain (her baby) through the pain. She now had a different way to view pain and unpleasantness. "It" did not "need" to control and "cause" her to displease God. In fact, the potential for bad feelings and the choice it represents (to please self and displease God or please God) was not fearful any longer. She had mastered the principle of gain through pain and found it gratifying.

As a good theologian-physician, your goal in seeing the patient won't be to function as a spiritual mechanic—praying with him, inundating him with biblical principles—or simply functioning as a body mechanic. Rather, it is to honor God by using your skills to bring about physical healing (if possible) according to biblical guidelines and presenting in a cogent fashion the appropriate truth of God in a form that the patient can understand and use.

Another "more" is your relationship with Christ. Because of it, you have access to the truth. Truth is one thing; accessible, useful truth is another. By virtue of your relationship with Christ, truth is available to you in the Bible by the Holy Spirit, and it can make you wise in the practice of medicine (2 Timothy 3:15-17). How, you may ask? I can think of several ways. One is ministering to the whole person. Since man is duplex, it makes sense that such things as "cognitive behavioral therapy" and "positive thinking" afford people relief. However, as a result of your relationship to Christ, you will be less enamored by this line of so-called "scientific reasoning" in favor of biblical truth. Another way is having the knowledge of the goal and purpose for life for you and your patient: pleasing God above all else. As we have said, pleasing

God as a good theologian-steward has its own rewards, one of which is improved health.

Since one result of sin is that everyone is born *out* of proper relationship to God and remains so unless radically acted upon by Him (regeneration), life without a proper relationship with Christ means:

- On earth, a hard life (Proverbs 10:24,27; 13:15; Psalm 16:4; 32:10)
- A future destiny of condemnation and eternal damnation (Hebrews 9:27; Matthew 23:33;25:31-46; Luke 12:5)

This is the bad news. However, there is the good news as well: helping believing patients understand the possibility and the surpassing superiority of pleasing God during their illness and the proper use of their failing bodies. This emphasis doesn't detract from bringing about physical healing but strengthens it. Patients may balk or even recoil at this thought. In some cases, the patient may simply be unwilling to take his eyes off self and a "now" approach to life. I have found that those patients are willing to rely on medications to relieve bad feelings and consider them as substitutes to a biblically-directed lifestyle. Medications directed to the problem may work well when the problem is organic malfunction or failure. Appropriate treatment often improves or heals the problem. But we have all seen patients who are "healed" (for instance,

Your Approach to Medicine   115

their RA is under control by all objective parameters) but continue to complain of symptoms. I suggest in these situations that you continue to pray and look for opportunities to present biblical truth. More often than not, those opportunities will come, and you need to be ready. More on God's kind of readiness as we move through the book.

In other cases, the patient may be unsure of God's way of viewing life and his body. He is ripe for raising the issue of salvation and the impact of his relationship with Christ in regard to medical problems. At salvation, something wonderfully supernatural occurs. The unbeliever is placed in proper relationship to God as a result of union with Christ. For the believer, I find that so many patients do not take their relationship with Christ seriously. They may be untaught, poorly taught, or rebellious. Knowing that they have an identity in Christ (remember, everyone lives out of an identity), how it happened, its cost, and its benefits is a great blessing and can be foundational for helping patients joyfully function as God's kind of patient.

Consider the "what" of the believer's relationship in Christ:

- The believer has fellowship with God because God is in fellowship with him. He knows God because God knows him (Galatians 4:8-9; 1 John 4:7-8). Yet some patients may say that they don't feel like God is close or that they don't feel God's presence. The problem is bad theology. How so? God and salvation are not an experience. God is, and the believer is saved. Both of those are facts. God is Spirit and not "experienced" physically through the senses. Rather, He is known by the exercise of saving faith (Ephesians 2:8-9). Moreover, you have the sure Word of God that testifies to both of those truths (Psalm 119:105). Dependence on God's written Word is far better than depending on one's feelings, experience, or perspective.

- Due to his relationship with Christ, the believer's *status* is perfect (he is a child of God: Romans 8:15-17; Galatians 4:4-7; Ephesians 1:5), his *standing* is perfect (he has no guilt or condemnation because he has been given Jesus' right standing: Romans 3:21-22; 8:1; 1 Corinthians 1:30-31; 2 Corinthians 5:21), and his *position* is perfect (he is a saint—one set part by God for Himself: Acts 20:32; 26:18). He has a new identity and a new operating agenda. As a patient, he can function as a good theologian-steward. In the office, the importance of these truths is especially seen in patients who tend to identify themselves with and by their past or their medical condition, healed or ongoing. Rather, as believers, God has singled them out as His children. That should make all the difference.

So, when hard times come into life, they won't fall prey to the mindset expressed by Rabbi Kushner in his book *When Bad Things Happen to Good People.* Faced with God's providence and a child with progeria, he concluded from his experience and by his logic that God was either not good or not powerful. God had to be one or the other. The rabbi chose to say that God was good but impotent and therefore limited. Based on his own logic, experience, and his view of himself, he attempted to bring God down to his level. His God was very small and he very large.

Patients can approach their physical problems in a similar fashion. However, a right view of the cross and God's love corrects that way of addressing life and hard times. A big God bought each believer with His own blood. He bled and died in the sinner's place. He went to hell on the cross. Those truths should help open the eyes and hearts of patients who are struggling under the weight of failing bodies. If God purchased them Himself and plucked them out of the pit of hell, will He abandon His children in the face of physical problems? The resounding answer is no (Romans 8:32).

- The believer is indwelt by the Holy Spirit. He has the capacity, inclination, and orientation to be what he was designed to be—like Christ—beginning now and completed in eternity (Ephesians 1:4). As a new creature in Christ, he thinks God's thoughts; he lives no longer for self but for God (2 Corinthians 5:14-17; Galatians 2:20). Instead of approaching medical problems as Rabbi Kushner did, the believer has a new lens to see and interpret life. The physical problems can be put in proper perspective. In the midst of pain, there are resources that most patients are unaware of. I had one lady tell me that she prayed to God for pain relief, and if it did not come, she took an anti-anxiety pill. After that statement, she stopped and tried to backtrack. She realized that she was saying that her relationship with Christ functioned as nothing more than a reliever of "anxiety."

Next, consider the expense of having a relationship in Christ—it is costly. Most patients are not familiar with this truth. Focusing on the cost of something can, and should, be a powerful motivator. While it doesn't cost the person anything, it cost God everything. The Father separated Himself from His Son as Jesus hung on the cross, the Redeemer of God's people (Matthew 27:45-46).[35]

---

35   Theologians call Christ's coming to earth His humiliation. The Son, sent by the Father, came to earth voluntarily as the God-man, out of a love for the Father and a desire to please Him (John 4:31-34). Jesus set aside His right to be worshipped as the glorious Lord of lords and King of kings in order to take on human flesh and become man – yet without sin (Hebrews 2:9-10; 4:15; 2 Corinthians 5:21). He lived under the law, was subject to the miseries of this life (not because of some sin of His), was crucified, died, and was buried. He was scorned, cursed, and treated as garbage and of no account. Scripture emphasizes the amazing love of God as preeminently demonstrated

However, once a believer, a person's relationship with Christ costs him everything. How so? It costs the believer *himself*. This is expressed in many different ways in Scripture. Six times in the Gospels, Jesus calls for a denial of self by picking up the cross and following Him (Matthew 10:32-38; 16:24-28; Mark 8:34; Luke 9:23; 14:26-27; John 12:25). Denying self doesn't mean denying yourself some object. It means putting off what *you* want and think is best. You are called to put to death self-pleasing. The cross is the instrument of that death. Crucifying self means putting an end to self-pleasing which is all that is within you that displeases and opposes God. Paul expresses the same truth in Galatians 2:20 and 2 Corinthians 5:14-15.[36]

By His actions, Jesus saved the believer for His own. Instead of self on the throne, God is the believer's Lord and Master. In terms of good stewardship, the believer will seek to make appropriate "life-

---

by the cross and our privilege of reflecting on it (Ephesians 3:17-21).

36   Galatians 2:20: "I have been crucified with Christ and I no longer live, but Christ lives in me. The life that I live in the body, I live by faith in the Son of God, who loved me, and gave himself for me." 2 Corinthians 5:14-15: "For Christ's love compels me, because we are convinced that Christ died for all and therefore all died. And he died for all that those who live should no longer live for themselves, but for him who died for them and was raised again." Both of these passages are mini-commentaries on Jesus' words in the gospel: those in Christ have a radically different motivation and agenda—as God-pleasers.

style changes" out of gratitude for his redemption. Often, patients that I see are reluctant to get "involved" in their care. For instance, impending surgery (such as a new hip or knee) or more aggressive therapy for, say, RA or Systemic Lupus Erythematosus (SLE) is rejected because of the cost, and it isn't simply financial. The reasons given are such as these: "I don't want to be a burden to my family;" "who will take care of my spouse when I am in the hospital for my surgery?" or "there are too many side effects."

There may be hidden motivations underlying most of the "reasons," which may be misguided. Usually it is loss of control manifested by fear and worry, and a general feeling of "not wanting to be bothered," which underlie a common basic theme—control. When it comes to deciding about therapies, I remind the patient that life and his situation is not simply about him. I have found that having a patient and the family remember the cross and its cost helps the believer to put these decisions in their proper perspective. Pleasing God from a thankful heart by being a good steward is a wonderful thing.

As physician, we are faced with troubling situations. Sometimes patients may have a simple problem in terms of diagnosis and even treatment. RA, diabetes, and hypertension can be simple diagnoses. However, the patient's situation can become complicated, and the patient may fail to improve. He doesn't respond to the usual and typical medications, and it's not because of non-compliance. At other times, patients are demanding, shortsighted, or simply arrogant and rude. I suspect this is especially true for patients who have so-called "chronic" diseases. The idea is that the "disease did it to the patient." However, some patients have the mindset and the corresponding agenda that health is a right and that the doctor is their vehicle for receiving it. When a patient doesn't get it or doesn't think he is getting it fast enough, his vertical focus is wrong. Biblical stewardship is not on his mind; if it is, it is only his ticket to get what he wants.

At other times, the diagnosis may not be clear, and treatment options are multiple. We all have had patients who stretch us in terms of diagnosis, treatment, and ministering to them. I can think of several patients over the years who present with failure to thrive, on-going pain, and abnormal but non-specific blood abnormalities. We make the diagnosis of vasculitis, aggressive treatment is instituted with a slow response but side effects develop from the medication and the disease. In these times, there is pressure, uncertainty, maybe second-guessing, even recriminations, and the patient may seek second and even third opinions. It is easy for you, the patient, and the family to be tempted to or fail to acknowledge and act upon what each is in Christ (of course I am assuming that all are believers). That proper vertical reference to life is vital. It is what drove Jesus onward to the cross (John 4:31-34). Focusing on the cross and the magnitude of God's love brings you face to face with the living God—*Coram Deo*. When God is rightly in the picture, each one should be motivated to function as a Christian should: by turning difficulty into blessing (our old friend of focusing on the gain in the pain and thereby using unpleasantness).

You are to comfort others as you have been comforted (2 Corinthians 1:3-4). Helping your patient, who may even become your adversary, to thankfully and even joyfully function as a good theologian-steward is offering God's kind of help (see pages 18-20 and the discussion on help and comfort). God's help (saving and enabling grace) is summarized by saying that truly needy people become aware of their true need, receive the gifts of salvation and growing in Christlikeness, and thereby use the hard and good times of life to do so. This is especially true in the world of medicine. Besides the examples that I have given thus far and those that are coming, especially in the final chapter, how would giving help look in your office? Obviously, your relationship to the patient and his to God will direct how you give help. No matter the medical issue and clinical setting (from a routine, well-check medical evaluation to follow-up for some cardiovascular problem to a maintenance follow-up), giving God's help is key. It may simply be a word of encouragement such as a Bible verse appropriate for the occasion, a time of prayer, a concrete and appropriate homework assignment that addresses him in his situation, or a suggestion that directs him to his pastor or some local church ministry of biblical counseling.

Properly motivated by God's love for you, growing in your relationship with Christ should prove to be valuable, even more valuable, to the practice of medicine than the "stethoscope" is to the cardiologist or the scalpel is to the surgeon. The physical "tools" of the doctor are just that—physical. As Christian physicians modeling Christ's earthly ministry (only to a degree as His was supernatural and redemptive), our focus is on the inside out. Bringing a patient through cancer or RA is a gift from God, but what does it profit a man if his focus is exclusively on the physical or having God at his disposal for relief (Luke 12:13-21)?

Being aware of the superiority of practicing medicine based on your relationship with Christ is one of God's gifts to you. Knowledge of the benefits of living out of your relationship with Christ will serve as an encouragement for you to practice medicine as a Christian. However, neither of these are enough. Simple awareness won't help you function as a Christian physician. Rather, application of biblical truth in a wise, courageous, and gentle manner is what I am talking about, and I think what the Bible teaches. It is important to be doers as well as hearers of the word (Matthew 7:21-28; James 3:13-18). In addition, there are many voices of counsel vying for ours and our patients' attention. We have already mentioned some of them (not an exhaustive list): medicine's pagan roots, neutrality, no forcing my views on others, time management, and at least one segment of the medical community whose goal is to have its mindset regarding the diagnosis and treatment of patients in every office. The battle lines have been drawn: will you be controlled by biblical principles, or will you side with these competing voices? The battle will continue until Jesus returns. Constantly reminding yourself and the patient that there is a better way, a surpassingly superior way, to be a physician and patient is necessary to practice medicine as a Christian. But it does cost!

Now consider a few of the benefits of having a relationship with Christ:

- It enables all believers to fulfill God's design for us, which is to be like Christ (Ephesians 1:4; Matthew 3:17, 17:5). We are provided with a proper vertical reference, thereby preventing so-called doctor "burn out"—that state of mind that leads one to give in and give up. We all grow weary at times, some of us more so than others. We could list a number of reasons. Yet Jesus, while weary as a man, continued to please His Father. Therefore, "burn out" is never an issue for the believer. Knowing that he is in God's will *and* doing God's will motivate the believer to fulfill God's design. Instead of burn out, there is a satisfying and contented life that surpasses all human understanding (Ephesians 1:4; Matthew 3:17; 17:5; Matthew 11:28-30; Philippians 4:7). Going home at night knowing that you have honored God is a wonderful way to end the day.

- The Christian has the mind of Christ and is enabled to think God's thoughts, desire what God desires, and do what God commands (1 Corinthians 2:16; Ephesians 4:24; Philippians 2:5; Colossians 3:10). So when you or your patient is faced with potential life-changing decisions, from so-called "lifestyle" changes to major decisions regarding life and death, you will have the courage and boldness to promote truth.

For example, how will you direct the dying patient and his family regarding, say, hospice? Will you agree that "dying with dignity" means heavy doses of medications that suppress any communication with loved ones and his God? How about your patient with Alzheimer's? How will you counsel the family? This situation is an anomalous one when the child becomes the parent. The parent grows increasingly more demented, and the child stands labeling himself as the caregiver. How will you direct him? Will his identity as caregiver replace what he is in Christ? And if so, what will be the consequences? How will you advise the hypertensive and diabetic patients who aren't compliant?

On the other hand, sometimes we think a meticulous patient is a good patient. Perhaps that is not the case. If that approach to his or her health is motivated by fear and an inordinate desire for good health, then the problem is a whole-person problem—first and foremost, a theological issue. These examples, and many more, call for solid biblical thinking and application of biblical truth. I don't have all the answers, but

God does. As Christian physicians, we have the mind of Christ and therefore must function like it.

- Rightly living out of your relationship with Christ produces the joy that comes from being released from the bondage of sin and seeking to please self. There is joy in serving a new Master (Romans 6:11-14; 10:9). So many times I see patients who are counterproductive in their pursuit of health or relief because they want it their way and now. The same can be true of physicians. How might that be demonstrated? The patient wants a diagnosis but not the one that you give him. What he really wants is a body that is not stained or cursed by God due to Adam's sin. That is not a reality this side of heaven. It wasn't for Jesus, and it won't be for anyone, not even believers. Yet, the patient functions as if that should be the case. The futility and bondage of having things "your" way (with its resultant grief) stands in marked contrast to the joy that comes from pleasing God. Your patient needs such joy to offset the pain that he may be bearing.

- An intimate and growing relationship to Christ provides a new perspective and focus on life. Focusing on what hasn't been guaranteed in God's Word only intensifies discomfort and discouragement, and it complicates life (Proverbs 10:24-25, 27-28; 13:15; Psalm 16:4; 32:10).

Focusing on pleasing God is always possible, is the best thing that you can do for yourself and your patient, and generally leads to a more pleasant life. The importance of this mindset can't be overemphasized in such fields as rheumatology (where pain and fatigue are regular complaints of patients) as well as hematology and oncology (where dying and death are ever-present). However, it is applicable, even mandatory, to all fields of medicine involved in direct patient care.

It is a non-negotiable fact that your patient is not at the mercy of his cancer or RA. A single cancer cell or synoviocyte won't grow or decrease without the direction of the sovereign hand of God who often uses secondary means such as medications and surgery to accomplish His healing. The cry is not for the cancer or RA to have mercy on your patient, but it is to trust a good God who has bled and died for every believer.

Consider the patient who may or may not want to check his sugar, watch his diet, receive another round of chemotherapy, or get another radiation treatment. Enough is enough, he says. You and I should never minimize the effects of a failing body, but we must maximize God's grace and the person's identity in Christ. The desire for relief or cure can be so overwhelming that it occupies the place of preeminence in a person's thinking. When that happens, the person is obviously being led by his feelings—the desire for good ones and the elimination of bad ones. At that time, functionally, the patient has minimized the Word of God, and what he wants is more important to him than what God wants.

- Focusing on one's relationship with Christ provides the constant awareness and acknowledgment of the fact that in your own strength you can't please God, but that in Christ all things are possible (Philippians 4:10-13). This is one of God's answers for the "how" of living with unpleasantness from whatever cause. A loving and providential God gives and takes away—grief should always be mixed with joy (Genesis 3:15-17; Job 1:20-22; John 16:20-22; James 1:2-4; 1 Peter 1:6-7). There is joy in pain because of what God is doing through you and what He expects *for* you—that you function by using hard times, including body problems, to develop Christlikeness. Such is one of the lessons of the cross—the grand demonstration of a loving and just God, keeping His promise to deliver His people from sin, Satan, culture's mindset, and self. Rejoicing in the Lord is a vertical activity that will never come in your own strength, but it does come as God's gift and blessing.

How would you see this worked out in your practice? Suppose that you have a person with a neurological disease whose activity is severely limited. His life is circumscribed; he is confined to his wheelchair or his chair at home. He still has medication to take, doctors to see (you and the neurologist), and blood work to obtain. But he says he is ready to "punch-out of life." He may mean it literally or figuratively. His mind-set is "life is the pits. Why should I stay?" So he may isolate himself in his room, on the computer, or on the bed or chair. He has shrunk his world such that only he is in it. What will you do or say? Will you simply agree with him and say his bad feelings and response to life is his disease? Will you simply medicate him and send him out after a pep talk? I have found that these five responses to life (fear. worry, depression, overwhelmedness, and bitterness-anger are fruits that stem from a basic desire—control. When things are not going the way expected and eventually demanded, problems look so big, and God so small. In reality, it is the person who is big in his own eyes and does not like the providence of God at that moment. Bodies fail when the whole person responds to life situations like that. The answer is a proper understanding of who God is, who the person is, and acting as if one's relationship in Christ means something about life.

How about the young woman with three children and RA who tells you that she just can't get going? These situations, in some form or the other, are heard daily. When the person is a believer, it makes all the difference in the world. Jesus encountered His three disciples who chose sleep rather than watchful prayer (Matthew 27:40-41). Jesus knew that their spirits were willing but that their bodies were weak. Failing bodies send all types of signals and messages to the brain, many of which lead to the person crying out, "No more! Stop!" The word of God says that you can do all things, i.e., please Me with your failing body (Philippians 4:13). What is impossible with man is possible with God. So, because of the motivation provided by the reality of being in Christ, within his physical limitations, he does function thankfully and sincerely. That is grace.

- Union with Christ provides the blessing of a clean conscience by the removal of the burden from the guilt of failing to please God (1 John 3:21; Romans 8:1). Your patient may wonder "why" and ask what God is doing (if he even mentions God) by giving him a failing body. He may think that knowing "why" somehow will lessen the problem. He may think that he is to blame or want to blame God, but he doesn't want it to appear that he is. He may "feel guilty" because of what he may or may not have done or should have done to prevent his problem or take better care of himself, thereby preventing it. The fact of the matter is that he has added to his problem. Not only does he have a failing body, but he complainingly questions (even attacks) God and His providence. His bad feelings may well increase. This scenario is so common in my daily practice.

More faith is not the answer. Rather, God is showing him the *better* way. It is repentance and reliance on the God of faith in order to please Him. God *deserves* to be honored, but it is so easy to turn from Him to self in hard times. The believer, in following the better way, is following Christ (John 4:31-34). That which rules his motivation other than pleasing God must be replaced by the desire to honor and worship God.

Consider the patient with a recent onset of aches and pains and maybe even joint swelling. She has enjoyed good health, but she has a mother with RA. This fact has influenced her view of health, RA, and what should be her lot in this life. She wonders if she has RA, what can be done about it, and how she can prevent or treat it. She tells me that she is a student of good health and wonders why she is in this predicament. In fact, she does have RA, but it is non-erosive and non-nodular – indicators of mild disease (RA can be mild). She ponders what she thinks she should have done to prevent it but didn't, and that which she did but now wishes she hadn't. She is beating herself up, judging her case with her mother's and feeling guilty, perplexed, betrayed, and even resentful that she is in her situation.

You determine that she is a believer and that God, not her genes or her past efforts and failures, have her right where she is. "Whoa," you say to her. She can complicate her rather mild disease by sinful thinking and wanting. As you treat her

RA, you give her biblical truth, not other medications, and the joy of being in Christ.

- When it seems impossible to please God *and* the prospect of getting a new body in this life is not possible, the cross demonstrates especially that God is please-able and beckons your patient to come to Him for rest (Matthew 11:28-30). Certainly rest is one prime necessity for your patient. He won't find *true* rest in medications. Many patients just "want it gone." Or they just want to "keep what they have." Often times they express the view that "getting old is not for them." All of these statements, and more that express the same thought, are theological statements. They have defined rest by the "now" and in physical terms. You and I can relate to that, especially if we have been patients ourselves, are aging, or both.

Simply moving the body (getting it going) sometimes seems (it certainly feels like it) impossible. Medications certainly can serve a good purpose, and the giving of them may be part of taking care of your patient God's way. However, have you considered the Bible's description of rest? It expresses rest in several ways. Rest for the Christian is not only a final destination—the eternal joy of being in God's presence. The idea of rest also has the meaning of aggressively waiting while remaining on this earth. So many believing patients that I see are looking to get out of the physical problem because they have lost sight of their mission—to glorify God in *and* with their bodies. They would rather have had God give them a different means of thanking and glorifying Him. Life may be an effort, but helping the patient focus on what God designed for him makes that effort doable and brings satisfaction in the doing (John 13:17; James 1:25). In an effort to "get through the day" or "get well" through a variety of means, they are seeking first *not* the kingdom of God, but their own desire In this way, trying to control the situation dishonors God and only leads to angst, both physically and spiritually.

How may that look in practice? In rheumatology, I see attempts at control in all types of patients, irrespective of the diagnosis. Usually, the patient describes symptoms as pain and more pain, fatigue and more fatigue. They have added to the problem by focusing on what they have that they don't want and what they don't have and wish they had. They have determined what the situation is and consequently focus on its hopelessness. They see no way out of the "black hole." They are on a merry-go-round and have concluded that there is no way to get off. The desire for a new body supersedes pleasing God by functioning as our old friend—a Christian oyster.

This is another time to say "whoa" to yourself and the patient. Please don't misunderstand. Treat aggressively the physical problem. And as I have said, good stewardship often means going to the doctor. But, God, through the doctor, often says "no." When God does, where do you and your patient go to find rest? Rest means relying on Christ's work rather than your own personal law-keeping of earning good health or avoiding bad health by what you do or don't do. I'm sure you have heard something like this: I can't believe I have this disease in light of how well I have tried to take care of my body. It is the mindset that good works (an American dream) result in what you want and have come to expect.

The Bible says that your once-and-for-all forgiveness in Christ means that you are dead to sin (its power—you're no longer under its mastery, its penalty and condemnation, or guilt) and alive to God in Christ (receptive to applying biblical principles). Therefore, you can and will please Him in spite of failing bodies and bad feelings (and perhaps bad advice). Rest is something you do—not in your efforts or even good stewardship—in the finished work of Christ. But, rest is also something that you have through your new identity in Christ—you are His and He is yours. That is a different but a true relief!

If a patient doesn't "see it that way," it is because he is filtering life via feelings rather than the Word of God. He does not understand or "accept" God's providence as purposeful and good. He spells "good" according to what he wants and thinks he deserves. He functions as a grumbler and complainer, not against his medical condition, you, or even life, but God. That mindset and habituation pattern is very difficult to break. But it can be done, and you may be the one to help your patient to do it. Such is the practice agenda of the Christian physician.

- Your relationship in Christ provides the blessing of knowing that you can and have pleased your God, which produces far greater satisfaction and contentment than any physical sensation (John 4:31-34; 2 Corinthians 5:7-9).[37] In those verses, Jesus and Paul point to a better way. Living *for* the physical and the now *by* feelings is so inferiorly undependable. Feelings, good and bad, are transient. As I pointed out above, patients who live by their feelings are on a roller coaster with no way to get off. Their striving only leads to energy expenditure with more fatigue and pain, no matter the physical problem. The Christian physician doesn't have to ride that roller coaster with him; he can help his patient get off! The

---

37   John 4:31-34: Meanwhile his disciples urged him, "Rabbi, eat something." But he said to them, "I have food that you know nothing about." Then his disciples said to one another, "Could someone have brought him food?" "My food," Jesus said, "is to do the will of him who sent me and to finish his work." 2 Corinthians 5:7-9: We live by faith and not by sight. We are confident, I say, and would prefer to be away from the body and at home with the Lord. So we make it our ambition to please him, whether we are home at home or away from it.

examples that I have presented and will present in the final chapter are intended to help you do that.

- Being in a proper relationship in Christ helps the patient get off the roller coaster of living by feelings. Living out one's identity in Christ simplifies life; it is less burdensome and complicated. Patients, and perhaps you, ask how that can be when their bodies are not working well, and they can't do what they want or think that they must do?

Go back to some of the basic truths. God's curse on sin will not be eradicated this side of heaven. Failing bodies and bodies that "I don't like" are a reality. There is an eternal perspective to life that changes the "now" and physical perspective of life. I have pointed out these realities to patients, and their responses are interesting: so what? What about now? How is that going to help me daily in my situation?

In view of this barrage of disclaimers regarding the importance of their relationship with Christ, what would you say? The major means of getting victory in situations like this is to help the patient acknowledge *and* act upon the purposes of God for him and his body. Each of us must ask the patient and ourselves, and continue to ask, what is God's purpose for us? What is life all about? Is it about my happiness or my holiness (growth in Christlikeness), for my pleasure or God's glory? Until patients come down on God's side, they will continue to be inundated with a tsunami of bad feelings with no way off the roller coaster of living by feelings.

A contented and satisfied life comes only when you live by God's truth rather than by your feelings, your own reasoning, or your own experience (Matthew 11:28-30). The last thing any patient needs is additional complications in life. How sweet it is to come to Jesus with a failing body and please Him by using that body to honor Him. Biblical truth and its application is not an anesthetic for pain and sorrow. It does provide God's reality and in that way offers what no medication or physician can—that is true healing![38]

- Because you are in Christ, you are released from the bondage of self-pleasing, hopelessness, and pursuing control by pursuing relief. Being a good steward-theologian is part of casting your cares on the One who cares about you (1 Peter 5:7). Proud self-trusters don't

---

38   God, in His wisdom, has provided in His Word countless examples of the inner and outer-man connection. I recommend these passages from Proverbs as a starter in your study: 12:25; 14:30; 15:13; 15:30; 16:24; 17:22. The thought presented here is that wanting, thinking, doing, and feeling are linked. As we have seen, Jesus taught that true healing begins in the inner man. A right heart towards God in whatever circumstance facilitates healing of the whole person. In that sense, an unbeliever can never truly be healed. In contrast, a believer will grow in his "healing" because he is being changed from the inside out, including using body problems to become more like His Savior.

follow Peter's exhortation. When you do heed Peter's "invitation," you acknowledge your creatureliness, God's control, and your reliance on Him. God blesses that approach to life. Given the natural tendency to live by the mindset of "I will do it myself," it is hard to cast your cares on God and others. That is because the focus is so much on self (1 Peter 5:5-6). Peter, in the two preceding verses, teaches that God blesses the humble and opposes the proud. Proud people are self-reliant; they don't cast their cares unless they think they can get something for themselves. Sometimes patients cast their cares on the physician. They expect you to do for them what God's grace is designed to do and what they should do as a good steward-theologian also by God's grace. By that I don't mean that they should not go to the doctor. What I do mean is that they may be asking the doctor to circumvent God's "no." Treating the physical problem wisely and aggressively means keeping the inner man in proper perspective.

This list is certainly not exhaustive, but its contents are awesome. God's truth affects you and the patient from the inside out by changing your thoughts, desires, and actions. As a Christian physician, you have the privilege of being motivated and guided by biblical principles for God's glory and to help your patient do the same, because both you and he are in Christ. Consider if every Christian physician brought his relationship with Christ to the forefront of his ministry to patients, how this would glorify God! The patient would benefit, and the physician would know that at the judgment seat he would hear his Master say, "Well done, good and faithful servant. You have been faithful with a few things. I will put you in charge of many things. Come and share your master's happiness" (Matthew 25:21, 23). As we continue, I will present practical ways to help you do just that.

Another "more" is God's relationship with you in Christ. Yes, you have God! Better, and more correctly, God has you. You are His and He is yours. That is why you have truth; Truth (Jesus Christ) has you by virtue of His relationship with you. The simple, yet profound, fact is that God exists. That foundational truth is under attack. Consider if God does not exist:

- Man doesn't exist. Rather, Scripture teaches that all being comes from God who is the Sourceless, Uncaused Source and Cause of everything.
- Knowledge and reason don't exist. Yet man does exist as an image bearer of God.
- Moral absolutes and ethical guidelines don't exist. But they do.

Your patient may wonder and hopefully ask, "Since God exists, what kind of God is He, especially in light of all my problems?" Great question! In order to answer him and help him draw a connection between his God and his physical problems, you must begin somewhere. That somewhere is the Bible, God's self expression, which proclaims that God is the Creator, Controller, Sustainer, and Provider of His universe. This God is a personal God intimately involved in the lives of His people. A proper beginning is a must for practicing true biblical medicine. Otherwise, as we have seen from previous examples, people will follow the thinking of such people as Rabbi Kushner. When you begin with God, who He is and what He has done and is doing, you should be struck by His awesomeness. Several descriptions of our God come to mind:

- God is independent, and He is self-contained. He is in no sense dependent on anything or anyone outside of Himself for anything. He has determined all things (Ephesians 1:4, 11; Romans 8:28-29). Therefore, for you and the patient the issue of control and trust is settled. You can look your patient in the eyes and gently but confidently declare to him that life is not out of control even though his feelings may say otherwise. And when he trusts God, his focus more easily turns to God's purpose for him to be God's kind of patient. Now you help him practice trusting God.

Author Jerry Bridges, in his book *Trusting God,* says it this way: "In this area of trouble of any kind, the Scriptures teach us three essential truths about God—truths that you must believe (*and act upon*) if you are to trust Him in adversity: God is completely sovereign, God is infinite in wisdom; God is perfect in love. Someone has expressed these three truths as they relate to us in this way: God in His love always wills what is best for believers. In His wisdom He always knows what is best, and in His sovereignty he has the power to bring it about."[39] (italicized emphasis mine)

Responding to physical problems with worry, fear, depression, and/or anger is actually distrusting God. It is tantamount to throwing a temper tantrum at God. It is competing with God at the level of power, wisdom, and love/goodness. It is, in fact, functional atheism.

Trusting a good God is what Jesus did and is what growing believers do. That trust may be demonstrated by functioning as a compliant patient, giving a simple smile and concern for others when feelings say "punch out of life," or being responsible (such as getting out of bed to go to work or doing exercises as a good steward). Imagine the impact of the application by both physician and patient of energetically and joyfully trusting God to medical care. Many aches and pains would be resolved, and many organic diseases would be less

39   *Trusting God When Life Hurts*: 1988; NavPress, Macmillian Publishing Company

complicated. Patient services would decrease, and doctor-patient relationships would change. The doctor and the patient could concentrate on the real issue of life: becoming more like Christ by functioning biblically even in a sea of body problems.

- God is absolute—He is self-sufficient. That means your source is absolute. He is the only standard for directing your life. He is the starting point and the reference point for how you practice medicine. You don't have to settle for relative and ever-changing speculation and philosophy. Yet this God woos you and your patient to come to Him for true help and comfort which He provides in His Son, the Holy Spirit, His Word, and fellow believer. As we have seen over and over again, people are seekers and will act on what they find.

It is easy to settle for counterfeit wisdom. However, we must remember that God is unchangeable. His plan, promises, purposes, and provisions don't change. The trust issue is further settled—God is trustworthy, a true Promise Maker and Promise Keeper. No matter his logic, feelings, or experiences, your patient is able to stare hard times in the face and know that his God will never leave or forsake him. His love never changes and He provides what we need in order to respond as more than a conqueror—knowledge, love, and energy (Romans 8:35-37). We know that God is in the problem, up to something, and that something is good in spite of the bad feelings and uncertainty. When hard times are viewed from that perspective, using them to rely more and more on grace naturally follows. Hope, which everyone needs, becomes and *is* a reality.

- God is infinite. In relation to time, He is timeless, and yet time exists at His command. In relation to space, God is everywhere, and everywhere that He is, all of Him is there. Yet, He is not space. We can't get away from God. He is our environment. He is everywhere, and everywhere He is, all of Him is there. Amazing!

Stopping your patient and having him focus on God's infinite nature should make him, as well as you, respectfully wonder and ask: Who is this God Who I am constantly confronted with? You can only conclude that there is no escaping God and that you are accountable to Him. With the psalmist, you can rejoice that "My time is in His hand" (Psalm 31:15). I can rest on Him for *and* by grace. He is my refuge and rock in my time of need. His presence *should* be a blessing—especially when feelings and logic say differently. "What does the Bible say?" is a much different approach to living with a failing body than making relief your top priority. God promises never to leave you or to forsake you or to place you in situations that you can't handle His way (Hebrews 13:5-6; 1 Corinthians 10:13). That is true hope! When bad feelings are seemingly rampant, it is not time to seek to take care of your body but to remember the cross as part of that stewardship.

- God is three-in-one: He is not made up of parts—He is only one God. And yet He is three-in-one. The Trinity separates Christianity from all other religions. Our triune God is mysterious – beyond all creaturely understanding, yet He is personal. He is self-revealing and saves a people for Himself (1 Peter 2:9-10). When faced with a failing body, there is nothing better than to know that you are His beloved child. How so? Salvation and sanctification are intra-trinitarian activities. As we have seen, the Father planned to save and to sanctify individual believers from eternity past (Ephesians 1:4). As the God-man, the Son saved His people. If Jesus broke His body for you, believer, He will not leave you with a broken body forever. The Holy Spirit applies what Jesus gained at the cross to the hearts of each believer. The Christian is secure in his salvation and sanctification. Failing, broken bodies won't last forever and can be used as God's instrument to fulfill God's eternal design of the believer becoming more like Christ. The believer must wait for the ultimate fulfillment of God's promise in heaven. But the hope of the promise fulfilled should motivate him to please God with the body that he does have now (1 John 3:1-3; see footnote 41).

As you consider your God, surely you must be struck by the fact that you have a very *big* God—bigger than you, your patient, and his problem. That makes all the difference for you and for him. However, sometimes the fact of a very big God is not acknowledged, maybe even denied, or His presence is "felt" as a burden. Such was the case with David and Job (see Psalm 32 and 38 especially verse 4 in each and also Job in 6:4; 23:2, 11, 16-23). Each case was different. David, a man after God's own heart, had sinned grievously but refused to confess, repent, and put on the fruit of repentance. He was under conviction of sin. Verse 4 of Psalm 32 and 38 describe one bodily effect of unconfessed sin. Today, that symptomatology would be called "chronic fatigue syndrome." (This is not to say that behind every symptom is an actual individual responsible for the symptoms. But there may be.) The status of one's inner man may have profound effects on the body. Job, a man who God called upright and good, was in great misery. He knew that God was "his friend," and because of his union with God, he did not understand why God was attacking him. In the end Job repented as he grew in his understanding of who God is and who Job himself was (Job 40:2-5; 42:1-6).

Yet another "more" is true hope. Every person, especially patients and doctors, needs hope. So what is your hope? Defined biblically, hope is the expectation that what God promised will come to pass. Because of the God of hope, we have confidence, and we are able to live as if God's promises are already being fulfilled—because they are! (Romans 8:26-27; 15:4, 13). They are fulfilled in Christ; He is our righteousness, holiness, and redemption (1 Corinthians 1:30). And they are fulfilled in the Holy Spirit; He is the first-fruit of our heavenly redemption and helps us in our weaknesses (Romans 8:23, 26). And they are fulfilled as the believer acts on His promises.

One place that is rich in God's promises is found in 1 Corinthians 10:13 ("No temptation has overtaken you that is not common to man. And God is faithful; he will not let you be tempted beyond what you can bear. But when you are tempted, he will also provide a way out so that you can stand up under it."). At least four hope-engendering promises are given by Paul: the commonality and universality of human misery, the faithfulness of God, God's power to limit and not exceed the believer's "spiritual IQ," and a way of escape. Responding to failing bodies with fear and worry dishonors God (actually that activity calls Him a liar; the verse teaches that a believer can't say he "can't"—God says so!) and robs the Christian of the hope that God offers in His Word.

Hope in the midst of a failing body comes as you look to God's purpose of wanting each one of us to identify ways that we must change. So a wise Christian physician will ask the patient, in some form, if his desires are God-centered or self-centered. What is the patient's (and your) chief concern:

to honor God or get relief? True hope and help begins and continues as the patient focuses on pleasing God. As the verse above indicates, the misery of this life is limited in duration so that thankfulness can accompany hope (also see 1 Peter 1:6-9).

Another hope-engendering promise is given in 2 Corinthians 4:16-18.[40] Hope comes as your patient focuses on the fact that misery in this life is only for a short time and that misery rightly responded to results in and is the result of Christlikeness. Failing bodies are not all that this life is about. There is a good God who deserves to be pleased. A correct understanding of Paul's teaching requires a proper point of reference and the goal for any situation rightly responded to. Paul compares this present life and its problems with that of eternity with all its joys. The believer has a window into heaven by virtue of the indwelling Holy Spirit and his growth in Christ who is our hope (1 Corinthians 15:19; Colossians 1:27).

Given the fact that God is a Promise Maker and a Promise Keeper, all facts of life and history point to Him, His plan, and the working out of it (Ephesians 1:11: "In him we were also chosen, having been predestined according to the plan of him who works out everything in conformity with the

40   For more on this verse see my pamphlet: "What to Do When Your Body Fails You": Redeemer ARP Bookstore, Duncan-Moore, SC. Also available online.

purpose of his will"). Like the old All State commercial, the Christian is in "good hands," but what a difference in the reason: because all of life is moving along at God's pace, according to His agenda, for His glory, and the believer's good. The believer awaits the fulfillment of God's purpose, eagerly looking forward to being in God's presence forever.

You might be asking, how might hope look in a patient? Another good question! Picture a child who is expecting a certain present and receives what he doesn't want. Compare him to the faithful housewife who is expecting an honored guest. What would you say to each of them? The child has his agenda and the wife hers. The child has expectations that were not met and most likely shows his displeasure. The faithful wife with much anticipation cleans up and gets her "act" together. Such is what hopeful believers do. They spend their time getting ready for the King. They are eager to see God glorified and will use their failing bodies to do so. Ground your expectations in what God wants. Like a child, the believer may focus on what he thinks is best. Like the faithful wife, the believer is to focus on pleasing God. Reciting and acting on God's promises enables you to evaluate and respond to life His way. The two views are generally mutually exclusive.

Biblical hope is realistic and never intended to minimize pain and suffering. Rather, it points to the greater good— being known by a personal God who saved you and promises to bring you home with Him—in His time. For another, the certainty of God's hope stands in contrast to those things that will not last. Good feelings and relief will not last. Remember, the believer has a pleasable God whose absolute control is working things out for His glory and the believer's good. The Cross and Christ's resurrection prove that fact (Romans 8:32). Therefore, there is satisfaction in this life, not in spite of a failing body, but because of who the believer is in Christ.

As we have seen in 1 John 3:1-3, these facts and the hope of seeing God face to face should be motivation for every saint to purify (set himself apart as unto God) himself as one of God's children.[41] What does it mean to purify (or sanctify) yourself? Purity is godliness in action and is summarized as conformity to God's will. Why is it the believer's purpose? (2 Corinthians 5:9)? It is because Jesus is pure, and God's purpose for every believer is for each of His children to be more like Him. We have seen over and over again what that means. In part, it means using hard times to become more like Christ.

---

41   See page 53 for a discussion of these verses. 1 John 3:1-3.: How great is the love of the Father lavished on us, that we should be called children of God! And that is what we are! The reason that the world does know us is that is did not know him. Dear friends, now we are children of God, and what we will be has not yet been made known. But we know that when he appears, we shall see him as he is. Everyone who has this hope in him purifies himself just as he is pure.

Let's not miss a corollary truth. The theme of joy in the midst of trouble runs throughout the Bible beginning in Genesis 3:15-17. The gospel was proclaimed after the fall and included the bad news: God's curse on Satan, man's labors, and the woman's desires and childbearing. God also promised Jesus' victory. Redemption and salvation are part of the fulfillment of Jesus' ultimate victory. We are always to remember that in the midst of pain (troubles in this life) there is always the promise of gain (growth in Christlikeness and ultimately being home with Christ forever). Therefore, our hope in Christ motivates us to look beyond the pain to the gain, using the unpleasantness of the situation to accomplish the greater good – Christlikeness.[42]

Consider an example of this principle in the office. A patient with osteoarthritis of the knee is asking, even demanding, pain relief. However, she has "refused" to lose weight, do her exercises (specifically quadriceps muscle strengthening),

---

42   An extraordinary teaching session occurred the night before Jesus went to the cross. That night taught the principle of gain through loss. In John 16:20-22, Jesus was readying Himself for the cross and His return to the Father. The apostles were stirred up within – they were deeply troubled (John 14:1, 27). There was uncertainty and perhaps a lack of hope. Jesus, knowing their weakness, pointed to the gain and a greater reality and necessity—the coming of the Holy Spirit—by using the example of pain and discomfort of childbirth.

and undergo surgery. What do you do? You know her and have discerned that there is fear of the hard work required before and after surgery, bitterness (often minimized by the term frustration), and the cry that she doesn't want to be a burden to her family. The bottom line is that she *is* a burden and will increase as one if she remains as she is. She doesn't like her body or her situation. In response, you don't minimize her situation; you maximize God's grace. Calling her to good stewardship means that she will rely on a good God to supply His grace in order to properly prepare her for surgery and her post-operative rehabilitation. Actively, at least, that means she gets busy doing her exercises and losing weight simply because those activities please God. The goal is not "coming through the surgery" but honoring God when she thought is was impossible to do so. In the end, she did have surgery, and she and her family are glad that she did. Did she learn that life is not about her but about pleasing God? I think she did—at least, she said she did!

So, when faced with physical problems, the patient and the physician are to look at the big picture. The greater good is to grow in Christlikeness. An important passage that I asked her to read and study was Philippians 2:3-4. (This was intended to be a "wake-up" call.) Paul is teaching the Philippians that a self focus leads to problems in the body: both the body of Christ and the physical body. Putting others before her in order of priority was a simple yet profound truth that she began to apply daily. And if physical healing comes or doesn't come, it is all of grace. For her to experience whole-person healing (inner and outer man) was a great blessing. Physical improvement must come as a byproduct of pleasing God. In 1 John 3:1-3, John brought together the amazing truth of God's love for His children and their response to Him.

In contrast, the unbeliever is devoid of true hope. He is his own reference point for life. He has only an uncertain, hope-so approach to life, although he may deny it. When God is removed from anyone's thinking, the only alternative explanation for being, knowledge, and moral absolutes is chance—uncertainty. Holding fast to uncertainty, the unbeliever has no hope, but he irrationally denies that truth. What follows is a downward spiral of discouragement and depression; he gives in to feelings, and eventually he gives up on life. Yet the unbeliever, and too often the believer, is not dissuaded from this line of reasoning. Therefore, he focuses on what he sees, reasons, feels, and experiences—the "now." The "now" approach to life is concerned with the "right now:" the temporal, physical, created, and personal. He has no recourse except discouragement, despair, and depression when a sovereign God doesn't give him what he wants. Then what does he do? More importantly for us, what do *you* do when he is *your patient*?

I vividly remember a patient who had a number of physical problems: obesity, smoking habit, bronchitis, osteoarthritis of the knees, and "fibromyalgia." Not only did she tell me the story of her physical ailments, but she reported failing relationships: marriages, parent, siblings, and neighbors. Her side of the story of her life included being sinned against (if her story was accurate) and reactive sinful responses. She concluded, almost triumphantly, that life was a mess. I agreed and asked her what next. She had no response. Here was a lady whom only the truth, rightly understood and applied, will set free. My job was to help her come face to face with the truth. She returned for a follow-up visit but played the same song, different verse. It seemed she was more interested in talking about her "black hole" than helping me help her climb out.

Too often the believer functions as if an unbeliever—as one without true hope. The believer may go to church, read his Bible, and pray. But when hard times come, especially in the area of failing and hurting bodies, he is only focused on relief and his God's ability to give it to him. He functions as if God is not to say "no" to him—ever. I wonder if he has been taught. I ask myself if he is relying on what he has been taught. So, I ask you: what is your response to this type of patient? Do you use the context of his medical problem (or potential medical problem) to provide him true hope? And if so, how? That moves us to insist on the Bible's definition of hope given above. The issue is: do I have it, and am I conveying God's hope to my patient to the degree that I should? Those questions are answered in the next "more:" help.

We have addressed help earlier and applied 2 Corinthians 1:3-4 (pages 17-18, 69). Part of the help that a believer gives is comfort. Both of these terms can be summarized by the word *encouragement*, defined as "speaking in ways that inwardly calm, strengthen, and urge one to perform some duty or task by giving advice about what he must do, and at times by offering other possible forms of help as well."[43] Comfort, then, is not simply sympathy or feeling the other's anguish. And Paul in 2 Corinthians 1:3-4 teaches that believers, having received God's comfort, can extend it to others. God's comfort can be summarized under three headings:

- The Cross: at the Cross, the bad news and the good news intersected. In His anger, God lovingly sent Christ to be His people's ransom price and to become sin for them. As a result, there is no condemnation in Christ; the penalty of sin is paid in full (Romans 8:1). The burden of guilt has been lifted, and the conscience is set free. Having been comforted, the believer comforts others out of gratitude for the Cross.

- Christ: caringly, compassionately, and diligently, Christ brought together divine love and justice (Romans 3:21-

---

43   *Encouragement Isn't Enough*, Jay E. Adams, Timeless Texts

26). He is God's righteousness, and He is the believer's righteousness by faith in Him (1 Corinthians 1:30; Romans 3:22; Galatians 2:16). Therefore, personal law-keeping in order to win or to earn God's approval is "out" as a way of life.

• The Holy Spirit: the believer, indwelt by the Holy Spirit, has the mind of Christ and is empowered and enabled to apply the lessons of the Cross in a Christlike manner. This is the import of the Bible's teaching in such verses as 1 Corinthians 2:16; 2 Corinthians 5:9, Galatians 2:20, and Philippians 4:13. In part, the believer ministers to others out of joyful thankfulness for what the Triune God has done *for* and *to* him.

Do you believe that the gospel is true comfort, not in some sterile way or only as an "away-from-the-office" mentality? Any other comfort is false. In Romans 8:35-37, Paul summarizes the freedom we have in the gospel by calling believers "more-than-conquerors" (or victors).

> *Who shall separate you from the love of Christ? Shall trouble or hardship or persecution or famine or nakedness or danger or sword? As it is written: For your sake we face death all day long; we are considered sheep to be slaughtered. No, in all these things we are more than conquerors through him who loved us.*
>
> (Romans 8:35-37)

This freedom and victory is because of the believer's relationship with God in Christ. Who works all things together for good (Romans 8:28-29; Ephesians 1:11). Paul spelled out the good of verse 28 in verse 29; it is to be more like Christ by virtue of all things. He spells out all things in verse 35. Gazing at that verse, the list you find leaves nothing excluded. All that life has in store, seven categories of God's providence, fits under one of those terms – including any physical condition that the patient, and you, will ever encounter. What is Paul's point? The believer is secure in Christ's love (not his for Christ, but Christ's for him). That security should drive the believer to view his body, all of life, through God's perspective. When that happens, he won't live by feelings but with the goal of pleasing God.

Actually, the believer is secure in two things: Christ's love and in the situation. Did you get the import of verse 37? In, not out of all things, the believer, and you his physician, are more than conquerors. At least, that means "these things" of verse 35 will not separate the believer from Christ or Christ from the believer. If his salvation is certain (and it is), then so is his sanctification. God enables him to conquer (get victory over, get on top of the situation) them. He is not alone; nothing can interfere with God's love for him. The purposeful, good God enables him not simply to "get by," "cope," or "accept." Rather, as a winner in Christ, the believer evaluates his situation through the lens of his good God who has revealed His purpose of growth as a good theologian-steward. That is truly good news! The circumstances may not change, but he changes in the circumstance. God's goal and agenda become his goal and agenda. Life is simplified.

Consider a patient I have seen recently—a young married woman who is a believer. She presents with pain, fatigue, obesity, and angst within. She knows that her body is not "right" and that she has been sinned against rather seriously. She doesn't draw the connection between her inner-man function and her outer-man feelings. As she tells her story piecemeal in the time allotted and in response to my questions, she concludes that, yes, she is in bondage—to this body that hurts so bad, to responding in anger and impatience, and to having what I call a "suck-it-up" mentality: "I tolerate pain, my husband, and my situation that includes those who have sinned against me." And yet her testimony, given through tears, conveys the fact that she considers herself betrayed by God as well as by others. And she considers herself powerless to do anything about things, even though she quoted a number of verses, including Romans 8:35. So what now?

She asked me how I knew so much about her and how I was able to ask the questions that I did. I responded, "The Bible tells me about people like you. And God is for the hurting and distraught." What a wonderful opportunity to be able to present to her how Christian physicians take their cue from the Bible and minister to the whole person! She began to understand that her physical problems were caused and/or complicated by how she had evaluated life and responded to it.

She faced a theological battle of epic proportions—*what is God doing in my life by sending all these sinners into it and mistreating me?* Once she answered that from God's perspective, she would also have the answer to the reason that God gave her the body that she had. Perhaps it was failing as rapidly as she thought (and felt). It took a number of minutes to help her unravel this. This "unraveling" is something that I have been trained to do and that I have trained myself to do. Time constraints didn't allow me to do all that I needed to do to help her out of her "black hole." But we made progress! As she leaving, she said that she "saw the light at the end of the tunnel. That light is the true Light, Jesus Christ." How would she love unlovable people? I asked her to read Romans 5:8. There she would find that the Cross was the answer—God loving unlovable people in spite of themselves. By beginning to love others, she was beginning to taste God's love for her and love, in a non-redemptive way, as He did (John 3:16). Having a body that didn't hurt was becoming far less important to her.

Don't misunderstand what I am saying. Improving a patient's physical well-being certainly can be a good thing. I thoroughly enjoy helping put RA into remission by appropriate treatment. Help does come from God's hand. But what ultimate profit does healing and relief have if you and the patient haven't grown in Christlikeness? In the last chapter, I continue to spell out how Christlikeness may look in various patient scenarios. An unbelieving physician can be a very good "body mechanic," but God expects much more from the Christian physician.

Another aspect of help is direction. Biblical truth "moves" the believer. Paul teaches this:

> *Paul, a servant of God and an apostle of Jesus Christ for the faith of God's elect and the knowledge of the truth that lead to godliness – a faith and knowledge resting on the hope of eternal life, which God, who does not lie, promised before the beginning of time.*
>
> (Titus 1:1-2)

We said earlier that truth is freeing. Truth, Jesus Christ, frees the person from earning good health, from seeking relief when God says "no," from the seemingly hopeless black hole of failing bodies, and from the angst of being sinned against and responding in a sinful manner. In these verses, Paul explains that the believer *knows* in order to live a godly life. And as a believer, he has the capacity and the indwelling Holy Spirit to enable him to do just that—even with (and because of) a bad body. See how Paul brings together knowledge, godliness, and hope. The key is God: He is a Promise Maker and Promise Keeper, and the believer is His.

Moreover, the believer's hope and help are stored in heaven, and the believer's faith and love are birthed in that heavenly hope (1 Peter 1:3-5; Colossians 1:5-6).[44] What is so good about that, you may ask (or your patient may ask!)? The context in which Peter writes is noteworthy. The members of his congregation were suffering or would suffer persecutions. In that sense, the people in our offices are similar. As we saw in the patient described above, problems abound. It is in this setting that Peter emphasizes security—these fellow sufferers have an eternal inheritance that is safe and secure. It, as are the heirs, was guarded by God. Consider Peter's dilemma. It is much

---

44   1 Peter 1:3-5: Praise be to God and Father of our Lord Jesus Christ! In his great mercy he has given us new birth into a living hope through the resurrection of Jesus Christ from the dead, and into an inheritance that can never perish, spoil or fade – kept in heaven for you, who through faith are shielded by God's power until the coming of the salvation that is ready to be revealed in the last time. Colossians 1:5-6: the faith and love that spring from the hope that is stored up for you in heaven and that you have already heard about in the word of truth, the gospel that has come to you. All over the world this gospel is bearing fruit and growing just as it has been doing among you since the day you heard it and understood God's grace in all its truth.

like yours and mine—how we motivate our patients to think vertically, thereby living victorious. His point: if God's "safe-keeping" activity included the heirs as well as the inheritance, then heaven looked very good. They were safe and secure in this present life even though humanly speaking it didn't feel like it or appear to be true (Hebrews 2:8-9). For Peter, and hopefully his congregation, an eternal perspective of their situation through the lens of their inheritance would be a powerful motivator for them to please God in their situation.

What glorious and awesome truths that God has supplied for physicians like you and me. God's desire and mandate for you is to utilize these truths in the most appropriate way to help your patient be God's kind of patient. What an awesome privilege and blessing! The last section of the book helps unpack the "how-tos." Practicing medicine as a Christian physician is a wonderful calling and ministry opportunity. Being aware of the differences between you and your unbelieving colleague and the "something mores" will help you embrace God's agenda for you and your patient. God bless as you do.

CHAPTER 4

God's Expectations of You

NOT ONLY DO YOU HAVE God's "something more," He has armed you (and every Christian) with all the armor that you need to battle physical problems and their effects. He calls you to use it and shows you how (Ephesians 6:10-18). God expects you to function differently from other physicians. Concretely, what are some of His expectations, and what do they look like in the practice of medicine?

First, God expects all Christians to be *informed*. One question that must be answered is the one of authority: what is your final authority for the practice of medicine? As we have discussed, God is self-disclosing and self-revealing. He has revealed Himself in facts that include such truths as the uniformity of nature; the laws of logic, reason, and math; the principles of physiology and anatomy of the body; and moral absolutes. But facts are not simply facts; they are His facts; therefore, they must be rightly interpreted and understood by His creatures. For that purpose, God has provided His Word through the Holy Spirit which teaches the meaning of facts from His perspective—the only perspective that matters.

God expects believing physicians and patients to function according to the facts as He has authored and interpreted them initially in the Garden. We have discussed some of those facts, beginning with a self-contained Triune God and His Word revelation. Having God as your starting and ultimate reference means, among others things, that the classification of diseases should follow biblical principles. I suspect that is a new concept for you. Let me explain. What God calls sin is sin. Otherwise, fallen man is the standard setter. Therefore, responses to life such as fear and worry must be considered in God's light and approached accordingly.

I have rethought such rheumatological conditions as RA, SLE, and fibromyalgia (FM) with God as my starting point. How so? Pain and fatigue are common symptoms in all three of those conditions. And yet sometimes there is no evidence of inflammation or degeneration in any of the conditions. It is assumed and even acted upon by doctors that symptoms such as pain and fatigue are part and parcel of the condition. We know that man is a duplex and whole person. Therefore, I am less quick to treat symptoms in lieu of gathering data on the patient's thinking and wanting. And after gaining the proper information, I present appropriate biblical truth and help the patient apply it.

Another area is that of behavioral issues attributed to various neurological diseases. This is an area that I believe needs further study. We see and hear about all types of behavior occurring in patients with degenerative neurological diseases. We need to consider how we should approach patients with that type of problem. At this point, I am making no recommendations. I am simply calling for biblically-controlled thinking in every area of medicine.

You might ask how God wants us to interpret such acute illnesses as tonsillitis, diverticulitis, and cholecystitis. In these situations, the acuteness of the situation and the potential for complications tend to garner the most attention. However, the patient is still a dependent creature who has need of a Savior and growth in grace. He is still called to be a good theologian-steward. The Christian physician will keep God's perspective in mind.

The doctor is a type of scientist. The practice of medicine includes understanding the body physiologically and pathophysiologically. We call fields of study like biology, physics, chemistry, and physiology "hard science" or objective science. Even the unbeliever is amazed at the complexity and genius of the body and the scientific studies that enable man to understand it. Certainly, every Christian physician should be skilled in his understanding of the body and in his field of expertise. In order for him to utilize that skill to full capacity, he must remember that true science—in this instance, the facts of how the human body functions—is, foremost, a vivid reminder and even revealer of God's existence and power and His wonderful creative activity and continuing ordering of creation.[45] Truly He is a God who is to be reckoned with.

An important truth emerges here. God has revealed Himself in the laws of physiology as well as the laws of nature, logic,

---

45   Theologians generally speak of God's revelation as threefold: special revelation (The Bible - God's written Word), natural revelation (God's created order including the laws and principles that are instruments for His control), and His Son (the Spoken Word). The created order functions like a megaphone – it declares God's glory and power (Psalm 19). Paul speaks about the necessity and clarity of natural revelation in Romans 1:18-20 which is suppressed (held down) in varying degrees by the unbeliever. Every person has an innate knowledge of God – the one true God and not some sort of god. Part of God's revelation in nature includes the laws of nature, math, logic, and in medicine, the laws of physiology.

and math. All of these laws speak loud and clear of God's control of His creation. (Natural man doesn't hear, let alone "see," God's existence and power—he attempts to hold down and ignore the facts about God.) The laws are the self-expression of God's will. Yet study as we might, all of "Him" (His will and the message of salvation) won't be revealed in these laws. That requires special revelation from the Bible. Study the "hard sciences" such as biology, chemistry, anatomy, physiology, and pathology, but remember that every fact is God's fact and must be informed by Scripture.

One area in which Christian physicians must be correctly informed is the origin of the world and man. The doctrine of creation makes it clear that God is the Creator and Controller of His world. He is the great Determiner. The only other option is chance, which plunges man into a morass of helplessness and hopelessness in spite of personal attempts to control one's own life. When the Creator is minimized or eliminated, it is because the creature has taken center stage. When that happens, there are terrible consequences in this life and in the next. Any so-called science that attempts to "disprove" the fact of a Creator and Controller God is false. A person may look at an apple tree and appreciate its fruit. Yet he says that its presence is because of mere chance (evolution). In effect, he is using one of God's creations (the apple tree) to deny God. Attributing facts that are due to God's providence to fate or "mother nature" (Hurricane Katrina, for instance) is not science. In medicine, attributing symptoms to that which it is not is also not science.

Another fact addresses the origin and nature of man (the doctrine of man—anthropology). As we have seen, man is God's image bearer and a created, dependent being responsible to God. He is no animal but the crown of God's creative activity. Any science that says otherwise is not true science, is false, and is competing with God. When science discovers God's truth in any of these areas and fails to acknowledge it as such, the scientist is the problem (and the one following) not science, the Bible, or God. As the examples show, the scientist attempts to use the fact of creation to "disprove" Him.

Remember, science and biblical truth are not at odds. They both originate with God. Practicing medicine must have its roots in biblical truth. The scientist gazes through his telescope and marvels at the vastness of God's creation; yet he proceeds, under the banner of science, to attribute all of it to chance. As he did with the apple tree, the scientist uses the fact of the universe and its vastness to deny God.

Not only do the hard sciences need to be informed and grounded in Scripture, but it is especially true for the "soft" or "social" or subjective sciences (such as psychology, sociology, anthropology, and philosophy). Because these social sciences overlap with the practice of medicine; have influenced medicine's view of man, his problem, and solution; and with the advent of the DSM-5, we need to seriously consider this subject. Unlike the hard sciences, the subject matter of the social sciences partially mirrors that of Scripture. The social sciences address such subjects as man's being and identity (who am I?), man's origin (where did I come from?), and man's purpose (why am I here?). They say things about the hardness of life, its causes, why man does what he does, and how man is to solve problems.

Their teaching covers the reality of pain, its cause, and man's solution. The soft sciences make observations and draw conclusions about man's behavior, feelings, and motivations. However, God in His Word (Scripture) speaks loud and clear about these issues, though not scientifically. In fact, these "soft" sciences are soft because they are trying to find out what God has already revealed. When the conclusions reached by the "social scientist" are contrary to Scriptural truth, they are reinterpreting God's truth and are in competition with God. For instance, in the area of pain, the mantra is that all pain is bad and every person has an inalienable right to have it gone or relieved. If that line of thought continues to be embraced, much of what the Bible teaches about using the unpleasantness of life for good and the principle of gain in the pain are functionally excised from the Bible. Another area that receives much attention is man's motivation. It is alleged that he does what he does because he *is* his past, his present, his genes, and his nurture. While the Christian physician is aware of the effect of influence and a patterned lifestyle, he does not accept non-biblical determinism as a legitimate explanation of why people do what they do. In the name of science, sin and God's answer for it have been removed from man's thinking. Practically, victimhood takes center stage. Taking on God in one's anger is considered "no big deal." Relying on the above conclusions discredits God, minimizes His Word, and complicates life. It is of vital importance that Scripture be your foundation for caring for patients if you want to practice medicine as a Christian.

As a result of the culture's mindset under the influence of the social sciences, victimhood has emerged as a leading cause of man's problems. And far too often and for many reasons, patients—Christians included—function as victims. Their bodies, their situations, or someone else is the cause of their problems. A victim mentality presupposes that life is about *me*, and God, if He is there, is to work for *me*. Patients are inundated by the reality of pain and the rhetoric that pain and bad feelings are somehow evil, undeserved, and that there is the potential of reversing bad feelings with medications, all for a better "quality of life." According to this view of man and God's world, a 2 Corinthians 5:9 approach to life is non-existent.

In rheumatology, I encounter the following scenario daily.

Patients present with malfunctioning and mechanically inefficient bodies from whatever cause—disuse, obesity, undisciplined bodies, damaged joints, muscle conditions and diseases, unwillingness to discipline their bodies, sinful responses to life, and/or a wrong focus and motivation for life. Accompanying comorbidity can add to the challenge and burden of helping the patient function as God's kind of steward. What do I do? How do I (and you) apply 2 Corinthians 5:9 (and other verses) in your office? Don't minimize that simple little question. You will respond; the question is how.

Certainly, taking care of the patient's diabetes and hypertension is a must. Then what? Remember, that unless the patient brings his thinking in line with biblical truth, his body will probable not improve, and, more importantly, he will not please God. One of the reasons for the practice of medicine is to help patients honor God by being God's kind of patient. As a Christian physician, you are on the frontlines in helping him. In fact, if you don't, perhaps no one will. In the following pages and the closing chapter, I use examples of patients with known organic disease such as diabetes and hypertension and illustrate "how-tos." Briefly, getting to know your patient, beginning with the physical but always working to the "inside" (asking about fears, hopes, expectations, and motivation), is one key for putting yourself in the position of effective ministry. By gathering information, you are also engaged in relationship building. You want your relationship with the patient to facilitate the giving of biblical, medical instructions. The medical issues are one thing, and his response to them is another. Both must be addressed. For instance, taking insulin or anti-hypertensive agents is one thing; being a good theologian-steward is another. In the same vein, rejoicing in the fact that his diabetes and blood pressure are under control is one thing; rejoicing that he is pleasing his God through good stewardship rightly motivated is another. But they are not mutually exclusive. Both are needed.

I'll give you an example from a case reported in *Internal Medicine News* (Vol. 43; #15, September 15, 2010, page 34) entitled "Topiramate for Weight Control." The article reported "the Problem:" A forty-four-year-old female nurse presents for follow-up of hypertension and elevated blood sugars. She is currently on lisinopril with a blood pressure of 142/94 mm Hg and a body mass index of 35 kg/m2. Her previous fasting glucose was 132 mg/dL, at which time you recommended decreased carbohydrate intake and physical activity. She returns to see you with a BMI of 37, a blood sugar of 140 mg/dL, and a hemoglobin A1C. of 6.1%. You diagnose her with diabetes mellitus type and discuss treatment options. She feels strongly about trying lifestyle modification. She asks you about drugs for weight loss. She reports to you that she has tried orlistat. You are reluctant to use sibutramine because of her blood pressure, and you have not prescribed phentermine. You recall a recent article about a drug reviewed by the Food and Drug Administration containing topiramate, and you are not familiar with the evidence of efficacy of this medication for this indication. The Question: "In obese patients with diabetes, is topiramate associated with less weight gain and/or weight loss compared with placebo?"

After reading the remainder of the report, I suspect that almost all doctors would agree that "good medicine" was practiced. My question: how do you define "good"? Where do biblical stewardship principles enter into the picture (1 Corinthians 6:19-20)? And are biblical principles, if used, just another treatment option? The questions I just posed, I believe, get to the heart of practicing medicine as a Christian physician. When you mention lifestyle changes, do you think biblically? How about the lifestyle of developing and manifesting fruit of the Spirit (Galatians 5:22-23)? Isn't one of His fruits self control? Taking care of the temple of the Spirit is a must—a non-negotiable mandate and privilege. How do you do so? Do you have confidence in God's Word that when His people apply His truth, they change? I am not suggesting a double-blind controlled trial with one arm of the study using biblical principles and the other arm "evidence-based" medical principles. I am calling for Christian physicians to understand the richness and beauty of God's truth, and then apply it to each and every patient.

Take another example. In those areas of medicine where no organic cause has been found, speculation and theorizing is the modus operandi for diagnosis and treatment. Yet time and time again, I find that patients are simply handling life poorly (sinfully, in fact). In lieu of presenting biblical principle as their only true hope for a satisfied and contented life (and more healthy to boot), medications are given—often in escalating amounts.

As I pointed out above, God's created order (and its uniformity, laws of nature, math, logic, and moral absolutes) declares God and His power. In a similar way, the "laws of physiology," discovered by man, point to and declare the Creator. Therefore, knowing facts about the body should drive you closer to the Creator. Knowing the science of medicine ("laws of physiology and pathology") must be filtered through biblical truth and applied in some form in all medical conditions.

For instance, sleep and its lack is a very common complaint. There is a plethora of theories regarding sleep and, partly on that basis, multiple medications are available. Thinking vertically, you will ask yourself: does the Bible say anything about sleep, and if so, what? And how do I bring my science in line with the Bible? (Not the other way around, assuming correct exegesis of the passages!) For starters, did you know that the Bible has much to say about sleep? [46] Briefly, the Bible says that it is God's gift to people, believer and unbeliever. If that is true, then sleep must be both a "body thing" and an inner-man activity. What holds a person's thinking affects his bodily activity including sleep (perhaps more accurately, bodily inactivity, although we know from sleep studies that there is much activity during sleep). For the believer, sleep and peace come because God sustains him (Psalm 3:5-6; 4:8). God grants sleep to the working man and those whom He loves (Ecclesiastics 5:12; Psalm 127:1-2). If you are familiar with the Bible's teaching, do you use the information, or do you functionally exclude God's material from your use? Sometimes it is so easy to prescribe a pill!

The number of patients who complain of a lack of sleep is increasing. When patients mention that lack, I move into my learning mode—I gather data by asking questions that move to wanting and thinking. In that light, I ask them what is going on in their life, and a follow-up question is "what is the last thing on your mind when you put your head on the pillow, and what is the first thought upon awakening, no matter the hour?" Depending on the answer, I point them to a passage such as 1 Corinthians 2:16 ("For who has known the mind

---

46   See appendix D for my teaching notes on this subject at Redeemer Biblical Counseling Training Institute at Redeemer Presbyterian Church in Moore, SC.

of the Lord that he may instruct him: But we have the mind of Christ"); they have the mind of Christ. They have the Holy Spirit. Therefore, they are able to think God's thoughts and make use of the gift of sleep that God has provided. Any of the day's unfinished business must be kept in its proper place. Lack of sleep is often a leaned behavior, and frequently it can be minimized or corrected by biblically-controlled thought processing (that is a proper vertical orientation to life via 2 Corinthians 5:9 instead of being directed by feelings, logic, and experience). Unfortunately, many patients are looking for relief without having to exert any effort to control their thinking. They would rather take a pill.

The overlapping of the Bible and the social sciences is also seen when you encounter a fearful, agitated, and discouraged patient who presents with a plethora of symptoms. These symptoms may involve the gastrointestinal, musculoskeletal, and cardiopulmonary systems. What is your response? I believe it is important to teach the patient about the body. What questions will you ask, and how will you direct the questioning? As we have discussed earlier, I have found that patients appreciate understanding the difference between signs (objectively measured and provable) and symptoms (subjective and non-provable). Sometimes the patient produces physiological changes in his body because of his response to something outside of him. It is amazing how often people function as a victim to something outside of themselves yet vehemently deny that fact—especially in regard to salvation and making a decision for Christ.

Most patients and even non-patients are not aware of this denial. So I have written the "pain papers" (see footnote 50 and page 110). Paper five addresses this issue. In that paper and during the office visit, I ask how something outside of the person "caused" changes on the inside, especially when nothing touched him physically. The majority of patients are clueless and don't want to be bothered by thinking. Apparently, many of them enjoy victimhood, which is so often learned. Others see the connection and talk about not being a reactive person. A few begin to recognize that they are in bondage to a person or situation. And still others are ready to break loose of their bondage and, in some cases, to do it God's way. That is when you need access to a church with a biblical counseling ministry; find one or become a trained biblical counselor yourself. You already are counseling.

Hopefully, from the preceding paragraphs, you appreciate the importance of asking questions that move you toward understanding the patient's hopes, fears, thinking, and motivation. When you do, you are firmly in the realm of bringing biblical truth to bear on the patient and his situation. It takes time and expertise—a full understanding of biblical truth so you can minister that truth rather than dispense it as you would medications. But the only other option is to function as a "body mechanic" and prescribe medications.

To truly help struggling patients who are overwhelmed, fearful, discouraged, and down, it is important to know what the Bible says about faith. Scripture emphasizes that saving and sanctifying (enabling) faith is a gift from God (it is never self-generated). If God is the Giver, then the believer is the receiver. God doesn't give bad gifts. Rather, the problem is the receiver's lack of faithful living.

What does it mean to "take the gift?" It means using God's gift by acting as a faithful child of God. Jesus makes this point at least four times in the Gospel of Matthew as He rebuked His disciples for being people of "little faith" (6:30; 8:26; 14:31; 16:8). They had failed to trust, instead choosing to give their allegiance to something else. In Matthew 8:26 and 14:31, the disciples' attention was on the storm and its effects rather than on the God of the storm. In Matthew 6:30, "little faith" was expressed in the context of seeking after physical things and living by feelings in contrast to seeking the kingdom of God. And in Matthew 16:8, the disciples thought in physical terms—physical bread—rather than in spiritual terms— teaching. Jesus cautioned them regarding the false teaching (leaven in verse 6) of the Pharisees. Faith is not the issue *for* the believer; the question is its expression. God is trustworthy. Jesus wanted the disciples to testify to that fact by being faithful people. In fact, Jesus expected His disciples to be such people. In each case, being faithful meant a right focus (vertically), right agenda (pleasing God), and right pursuit (the application of biblical principles in response to God's providence horizontally) of it.

Faith in faith is not a biblical construct. The issue for the believer is not more faith. When your patient brings up the subject of faith, ask, "How much faith is needed to be healed or get relief?" and "What is wrong with the faith that you have?" These interesting and thought-provoking questions are geared to patients who are trying to generate something from within in order to be cured or to get relief. They envision God as a debtor God—one with whom to bargain or from whom to earn favor. Such was Rabbi Kushner. His standard for fairness was not the Cross; it was based on what he thought he "deserved" and what he thought a "good" God was.

The answer for your patient is that, for the believer, the problem is not mere faith or even more faith. The problem is not faith (the gift) or God (the Giver). God never gives "bad" or defective gifts (Ephesians 2:8-9). The problem is the receiver of the faith and his lack of faithfulness in its use.

Some teaching is in order. Salvation is not a free ticket to get a non-failing body. That blessing awaits the believer in heaven. In the meantime, the believer is to prove faithful as His God has proven Himself to be faithful. How does he do that? He remembers the Christian oyster metaphor. The believer uses his body problem to become more like Christ. He reminds himself that pain and gain are always linked just as the bad and good news are linked (Genesis 3:15-17). Something better awaits the believer—on this earth the joy and contentment of pleasing God and in heaven being in the eternal presence of God with a glorified body. Your body and its bad feelings may "tell" you something different, but God's Word holds the key to "everything that you need for life and godliness" (2 Peter 1:3-4). God honors faithful people in this life and the next (Matthew 25:21, 23). As Christian physicians, we help our patients understand and act upon that.

So how do you help patients? As we have said, it is different for every patient and his situation. However, the core principles are the same. First, determine the patient's salvation; is he saved or not? Next, if he is saved, determine his view of Christ's relationship with him. You do that by determining the impact of who he is in Christ upon his attitude and action. Asking questions is a key in finding out. If he is saved, then I often go to such passages as Matthew 7:21-28 and James 3:13-18. The import of those passages is to determine is he is a hearer only or a doer. This takes time. And yet as you become more and more convinced regarding the practice of medicine, you will find that it doesn't take as long as you think, and it has great rewards—for you and your patient—and it honors God.

Consider the following example. A middle aged, overweight woman bitterly complained of pain and fatigue; "I can hardly go and do." As I asked her questions, I garnered the following information: she eats for comfort—to avoid bad feelings and have good ones. This was a learned behavior for handling problems—"stress," as she put it—since her teens. She expressed her behavior this way: "I seek refuge in food. I escape into the world of feeling better. But it isn't working." As we talked, she was willing for me to summarize what I heard and offer my interpretation. She was a reactive person, controlled by the pressures of life because of her desire for pleasure in the form of peace, security, and certainty. Things had to be a certain way, and when they weren't, she did not like it. She would do anything to avoid bad feelings and to have good ones, even though the good feelings didn't last, her body was suffering, and she was not pleasing God. She agreed that she was a slave and in bondage to seeking pleasure. She did not tell me what made peace so important to her, but she was listening. At the end I offered another assessment: "you are competing with God and at a basic level, your obesity is a theological issue."

She sat there and after a long minute agreed. Her behavior was saying that it was okay for her to seek refuge in something other than God and thereby escape worshipping God. She chose to worship self. What was sadly ironic was the fact that she had so many excuses for satisfying herself but so few reasons to glorify God in and with her body.

At this juncture (all of the above transpired in less than eight minutes), she was in dilemma; was she a hearer and a talker or a hearer and a doer? She rightly understood that her eating was a learned behavior. She had functioned as if life (actually God because of His control) was the problem. Her mindset was "I am not the problem. I deserve to have good feelings and avoid bad ones." She had been exposed. It was almost a relief for her. But we weren't finished. I offered reading material for her (in her case John 8:31-32 due to her bondage and 1 Corinthians 10:13 for her to stay in God's way). I offered to meet with her, and she promised at least to call with a progress report and her decision.

A second expectation of God is growth—both individual (of the believer) and corporate (of the body of Christ). God expects *growth*—not perfection (2 Peter 3:18; Philippians 1:9-12; Colossians 1:9-10). This is growth in Christlikeness. The Bible likens it to undressing and dressing (Romans 13:12-14; Ephesians 4:22-24; Colossians 3:8-10). The believer aggressively and actively puts off old habits of self pleasing by replacing them with new habits of pleasing God.

Too often, patients who are struggling physically may be

struggling spiritually. That is to be expected, because man is duplex. The above patient is just one case in point. In response to their situations, they often isolate themselves from God, from their immediate family, and from those in the body of Christ. Escapism is one consequence of living by feelings rather than biblical truth. At least one of the physician respondents to my questionnaire appreciated the value of God's people ministering to God's people. Consider your community demographics by asking what church ministries and resources that address both physical and spiritual needs of your patients are available. Otherwise, ministry will be left to the government (local, state, and federal) and will, of necessity, limit or eliminate the cause of Christ. You will need to decide if, and how, you get involved. It may tricky. Take hospice, for example. My experience in two states has led me to conclude that their goal is not to minister to a patient's soul but to provide relief to the body. Christian MDs shouldn't expect hospice to broach the subject of eternity from a biblical perspective; it's up to the Christian physician to minister to the whole person—in spite of medications and rules. So, know your hospice people and be prepared to give biblical guidelines on how you want your patients cared for. The patient's last days may be his final time to address issues with God and others. Therefore, use the time wisely (Ephesians 5:15-18).

These truths are *not* esoteric. They come from the written Word of God. The Bible is not just another book. And God and His Word can't be ignored. God won't have it any other way. So how do these truths apply to the practice of medicine? We can summarize the truths presented throughout the book under the heading of God's sovereign will and His complete control. This truth is basic to a proper understanding and response to all of life but especially in the ministry of the practice of medicine.

Consider this metaphor. A cowboy seeking health insurance was asked if he had had any accidents. He demurred and said "no." However, he did say that he had been thrown from a horse and bitten by a rattlesnake. The insurance agent retorted that those certainly must have been accidents. The cowboy responded by saying, "no sir, both of them did it on purpose."

The story highlights the point that the God of history so controls His world and His creatures that nothing is an accident. Christians may never make excuses or apologize for God's control of His universe. God is in control even if it doesn't appear from our perspective that He is (Hebrews 2:8-9). Scripture is replete with illustrations of this fact: Job, Paul (Ephesians 1:11 and 2 Corinthians 4:1-10; 6:4-10; 12:7-10), Isaiah (14:27; 46:10), and Nebuchadnezzar (Daniel 4:35). Your patient with his problem is no more out of God's will and plan than those mentioned in Scripture. That ought to be a source of hope, comfort, and encouragement for him and you.

As the Sovereign Creator and Controller God, our Lord initiates and brings things to pass for His glory and the good of His people. All of history is His story documenting His plan, presence, and purpose for His world and His creatures. He has the right and authority to do just that. He is God, Creator, Controller, and Sustainer of all of life including physical problems. Therefore, God is to be reckoned with. Everyone lives in the presence of and in relationship to God, whether he acknowledges it or not. That vertical relationship is expressed horizontally as he lives in faithful and humble submission to God or as a rebel, interested in getting from others, God included. An accounting is due at the judgment seat of God.

How is God to be "reckoned" with? As the previous example showed, the patient's eating was a theological issue. She had chosen to serve herself functionally and ignore the God of the universe. She was engaging in serious business. She was living proof of the validity of Proverbs 13:15 (the way of the unfaithful is hard). When I helped her realize what activity she was engaged in, she had hope. That was a start. She had a life patterned on living by feelings that only grace could change. God's grace had changed her at salvation, and yet she still functioned as an unbeliever in this area of her life. I will have another opportunity to continue helping her when she returns for her follow-up visit. I have been praying that what she hears from the pulpit and what she reads in her devotional time will reinforce the truths presented to her in the office.

Since God is her environment (He is around us, in us, and with us), His handiwork is everywhere. She was created as His image bearer and as believer recreated in proper relationship to Him. Therefore, it is impossible for her to ignore Him. Try as she might (she agreed that she was both competing with and running from God), she can't stop being God's creature. At any moment a believer has only one of two choices: embrace God or functionally reject Him. The latter you do at a grave risk—not only eternal condemnation but temporal misery of varying sorts and with varying proportions (Proverbs 13:15). So you ask what the sovereignty of God has to do with the practice of medicine. Everything! In summary fashion, based on God's sovereignty, let me remind you that:

- You are a Christian and a physician by God's plan.
- You have patients, also by God's plan. And He has a plan for every patient that He sends your way.
- God has a purpose in bringing about all things. One of His purposes is for you as a physician to understand that life is not about you or your patient.

Hopefully you agree with the truths laid out throughout the book and summarized here as God's power, control, and authority to "run" things His way for His glory and the patient's benefit. Therefore, practicing medicine His way is crucial. How do these truths help you do that? That question returns us to the issue of an apparent disconnect in the thinking of doctors (even Christian ones) between a patient's spiritual life and his physical problems. The modus operandi of fallen man is to understand life, the origin of problems, and problem solving without God. He can't do otherwise. As a result, in medicine and among doctors, there is a dualistic disconnect between biblical truth and scientific fact. I attribute some of the disconnect to medicine's pagan roots. Historically, it is clear that the vigor of the disconnect intensified when Freud came on the scene and opened his office on Easter. That day ushered in a radically different view of man, his problems, and their solution. The attempt was to render the gospel impotent. It had, and so it is today, no part in solving the "deep" issues of man's life. That mindset has grown in exponential fashion over the last one hundred years.

However, that can't be the only reason. Medicine and perhaps many non-physician Christians including pastors don't seem to understand God's creational design of man as a duplex unit. Rather, they are quick to look to some other authority, whoever or whatever that may be. It is usually the "expert." What follows is the lack of applying biblical principles to patient care. Today, especially, it is so very easy to view the practice of medicine through the lens of medical science or some facsimile rather than through the lens of the Bible.

The "soft sciences" have taken their own observable facts of man and have developed a philosophy of motivation presupposing that the Bible is devoid of one. They are competing with God. Science has chosen to answer why man exists and why he thinks what he thinks and does what he does or doesn't do. Why is that? The Bible, our ultimate reference point, teaches that unbelievers at their core (and unfortunately, many functional believers) are anti-God in principle. They accept man's truth and the so-called scientific view of man trying to explain what God is doing and has done in some other way. This view is multifaceted and runs the gamut of man as an animal, a victim, and a seeker (such as happiness, an inner connectedness, and a higher life, to name a few). At his core, the unbeliever is inherently a liar and a deceiver beginning within himself. He suppresses the truth of God by his unrighteousness (Romans 1:18-21; 2:12-16). Medicine and science apply human reasoning without God at the center (or even at the periphery). What we need is a Copernican revolution in medicine with Son at the center of the practice of medicine (not the sun). He, not man, is at the center of the universe.

As I pointed out earlier, I did practice with a physical-spiritual dualism and Bible-science disconnect as both an unbeliever and believer. As an unbeliever, that comes as no surprise. I did what I did because I had nothing better to offer. I thought I was helping people. However, I was ignorantly, arrogantly thinking that I had the right to define help my way. As a believer, I was arrogantly ignorant. I still thought as an unbeliever. It took me some time to determine that God had different expectations of me and my patients than I did. Victory in Christ secured at the Cross motivated me to a right understanding of the body and its relationship to the inner man. Then I was able to minister to the whole person physically and spiritually, and I continue to do so.

Not every patient and doctor appreciate this approach. Some patients simply reject it outright and seek "help" elsewhere. I had to count the cost. Others are aware that I know rheumatology, and they want "physical help." They make it clear that I could take care of them on their terms.

Initially, I reacted by thinking that I "must" force the issue (our friends "force" and "help" that we have discussed previously). When I did function as such, many patients were turned off and rejected me and the message. The problem was me, not them. God had me right where He wanted me. I was having a crash course on who was really in control. I humbly determined that God had been gracious to me. I repented in the areas I needed to and sought Godly counsel. I came to understand that I was to be His instrument for change but not a hammer! I learned the lesson that Samuel learned (recorded in 1 Samuel 8).

Samuel was concerned that Israel was rejecting Samuel

when they cried out for a king. God taught him that Israel rejected not a man, Samuel, but God. Samuel was God's instrument. Samuel understood and was a faithful servant. I got the message. It was not me but God that patients reject. As a result, I became aware of who I am and why patients come to the office and continue to come to this very day. The patients view me first as a doctor and have no idea that biblical principles have a role in helping him get victory (evidence for the disconnect).

I have made mistakes along the way, such as attempting to present God's truth before I had established a vital relationship. I assumed that believers wanted help God's way and that their definition of help and God's definition of help was the same. More times than not, it wasn't. Sometimes I was able to explain the difference, But at other times the patient didn't want to hear.[47] It was, in part, out of this situation that I developed the "pain papers" (see footnote 50 and page 102). They enable me to introduce changed thinking and its salubrious effects on body problems and open the door to a dialogue regarding being God's kind of patient. Sometimes the pa-

---

47   I have reiterated that God defines help as bringing truth to the person that frees him from his bondage. Part of that truth, especially for the practice of medicine, is that living by feelings is counterproductive to good health and a satisfied and contented life. Rather, living by the Word of God is God's design for believers and has its own reward.

tient takes to heart the principles in them and asks questions, opening the opportunity to "ease" biblical truth into his situation. I included a paper entitled "Is There Something Better than Positive Thinking?" (The secular world borrows—really steals—from God's creational design, doesn't acknowledge it, but makes use of it to "help" the person feel better. This activity is tantamount to the example of the apple tree as a good fruit-bearer to enjoy and utilize but not for declaring the glory of the Creator.)

Other mistakes I've made include thinking that I had "to tell" the patient things instead of asking questions and learning where the person was, not only medically but in His relationship with God in Christ. A major mistake was not appreciating the fact that hurting people have their own agenda and any deviation from it offered by me (or anyone) would be construed as an attack on them. I realized that self-deception was (is) common and often covers up an agenda of getting "for me and my benefit." I bring God into the picture at every opportunity. Sometimes it is in passing, such as when viewing a radiograph with a patient and pointing out God's creative activity of the body. Sometimes it is because God's truth is most needed. I have learned that questions prick the conscience, and accusations tend to harden the will. Therefore, I have become a good data gatherer and have learned (and continue to learn) how to use the data to bring biblical truth to bear on the patient. More examples are coming in the final chapter.

I changed (it was gradual) when I acknowledged the result of God's curse on mankind in myself and my patients. Patients had bought Satan's lie and brought it with them when seeing me. They functioned as if they knew better than God, and me, about their body. As a consequence of their sinful responses to His providence, physical problems resulted or were made worse.

What are some of Satan's lies? Primarily, it is that life is "theological" as he defines it—"me first reaching to please self." In essence, "I am god." As a corollary, another of Satan's lies is that you get what you want by living by feelings for the "now" and "forget" eternity. Right now is what counts, and you do so by the pleasure principle.

God's truth says that the Bible is about motivation (in contrast to a secular approach to caring for patients). At a basic level, people are motivated by the childlike goal of "what is in it for me." For patients who are resistant (or are clueless) to hearing and applying biblical truth, I often ask the Proverbs 13:15 question: what has your way of handling life, body and all, accomplished (gotten you)? Usually, patients will reflect, and if the pain is more than the gain, they are willing at least to dialogue. However, often patients are comfortable in their discomfort. That is an interesting phenomenon. Sometimes people are ignorant and hopeless, and at other times they consider that the effort for change is not worth the effort. They have lived a patterned life of self-pleasing and are not willing to discipline themselves for the purpose of godliness. They fail to recognize that they have theological issues that are, in part, playing out in their bodies. In spite of my failures, God has been gracious to me and my patients. So, too, will He be with you and your patients as you seek to practice biblically-based medicine.

God expects His child to become more like His perfectly obedient Son by trusting and obeying. Not only does the believer have Christ as his Savior/Redeemer but as his Lord and Master (Romans 10:9). And Christ is some kind of Master/Boss! Christ modeled the agenda set for every believer in eternity past: to please God and to live a truly contented life in conformity to Him (Ephesians 1:4; John 4:31-34; 2 Corinthians 5:7-9). Throughout the Gospel of John, we read of Christ's motivation for life: His intimate relationship within the God Head. From that covenant relationship flowed His dependence on, love for, and desire to please the Father by doing His will (John 3:35; 4:31; 5:20, 30; 6:38; 8:26; 9:4; 10:17-18, 37-38; 12:48-50; 14:31; 15:10; 17:4). Jesus was empowered by the Holy Spirit (Isaiah 11:1-4; Luke 3:31; 4:1). So too, is the believer via the Holy Spirit and His Word (Philippians 4:13; 1 Timothy 4:7-8). There is much theology here. Suffice it to say that Jesus' life summarized what living as a God-pleaser looks like. He put it in a nutshell the night before He died by stating a non-negotiable truth: if you love Me, you will obey my commands (John 14:15, 21, 23). Loving Jesus meant love for the Father (and Holy Spirit). At the least, obedience means thankfully—and sometimes courageously—applying biblical truth and principles daily, both in and out of the office.

As you know, when bodies hurt, it is easy to give up on pleasing God and give in to being directed by feelings. Sometimes simple tasks such as getting up and out of bed or doing chores seem monumental. If Jesus gave into mere feelings, what would have been the results? They are unthinkably hellish; if there had been no humiliation or exaltation, there would be no salvation. But! He didn't give in, and there is salvation! Pleasing the Father and modeling Christ should be the *modus operandi* of every Christian physician, regardless of the patient's physical condition.

The truths expressed in these paragraphs are especially tailored for the burdened patients. However, God's empowering is often misunderstood. A most common idea is that "my body has to be in good condition (measured by feelings) before God will use it for His glory." The Bible's answer? Tell that to Jesus and Paul (Isaiah 53:1-12; 2 Corinthians 4:8-10, 16-18; 6:1-10; 11:23-28; 12:7-10)! God doesn't "agree" that a failing body is useless and of no value. Rather, failing bodies are an opportunity to practice and to minister life-changing truths. How, you might ask? It is both by actions and words. For example, the Psalms are full of prayers that acknowledge hurts and cry out to God for help. Those prayers may well be expressions, not of complaints but of a growing trust in and reliance upon God and His promises. When the believer "suffers well," others around him may be drawn to God (not to the patient) as a result. God's purpose is fulfilled when even one of His children are plucked from the fire of hell by the example of faithful living of another.

Both written and spoken words may be powerful motivators for growth (2 Corinthians 1:3-4). The "hurtee" becomes the encourager—a type of Barnabas (his name means encourager, and he was just what Paul needed). Remember that truth and life are the springboard for the church's one-anothering ministry. Facing a hurting body biblically and helping a person do that as well are wonderful things. Thinking is changed, an eternal perspective becomes more of daily perspective, and growth in the inner man is more highly cherished (James 1:2-4; Psalm 119:65-71; 2 Corinthians 4:16-18; 12:7-10). The patient and the helper minister to one another as well as to others.

Depending on your specialty, most patients are burdened and their lives complicated. Many people with failing bodies interpret God's providence as an "I don't like" or an "I don't deserve" situation. When bodies hurt and uncertainty is swirl-ing all about, it is easy to function as if God owes them—a better body, relief, or a change in the situation. It is at this time that the stage is set for you. You have stepped into a theo-logical battle of major proportions. Essentially, the patient is not a happy camper and wants to know why God isn't treat-ing him better than He treated Jesus Christ. As the examples have shown (and they are more to come in the final chapter), biblically-based medicine can, and should, be a reality in your practice and mine. I encourage you to begin vertically. Prop-erly bring God into the picture, as He is already there. Unless the patient acknowledges that he has a relationship with God, and that his God is good, big, powerful, and purposeful, he will only evaluate his problems through his own grid. Only when he re-interprets his situation in light of God's truth will he be able to respond to the unpleasantness and pain in faith-ful trust and obedience to God. Then he will be God's kind of patient simply to honor God.

As part of God's third expectation, growing yourself and helping the patient grow in Christlikeness, you will need to think through the implications of the patient's conclusions from God's perspective and help him to reinterpret his physi-cal problems according to biblical truth. If you do not, you will only generate "symptomatic" therapy that has little long-term success. Even if the situation changes by God's power, the patient is faced with several questions:

- Is God really there when it doesn't feel like it?
- Is His promise to never leave me or forsake worth it? Is it the answer?
- Is God trustworthy when my feelings and others cast doubt on the fact that God has the best interest of His people in mind?

So how would you do that? As the examples have shown, failing bodies or the prospect of one is a theological issue. The question asks if God is trustworthy. It is one thing to say that He is and another to act on that truth. God is trustworthy— the Cross and the resurrection prove that He is. The issue, then, is the patient and who he depends on: himself or God. Depending on self may take many forms: an unthankful spirit as shown by grumbling and complaining, wondering why the doctors can't fix him, asking why he has to take medicine or to practice "lifestyle" changes, or blame-shift by saying that he has a right to be unloving or get frustrated because he hurts and doesn't feel good. Many times, as I have said, patients are copers, acceptors, grin-and-bearers, or toleraters. In my pain papers, I call these patients "couch potatoes." There is much inertia (really resistance) in their life – physically and spiritually. On the other hand, self-trusting can take the form of the "road runner." These people are on the go; they tell you about all their responsibilities and the need for a body that works well. They lament, "I just have to have a different body, one that feels better and that will allow me to do what I need to do."

In contrast, the God-truster says, "Whoa, I am in a theological battle. Living by feelings for my sake doesn't please God. My goal is to please Him, which is best for me because it glorifies God. I will use this situation (whatever it may be) to be responsible and kind and to minister to others the way I can." It is not that feelings are ignored. As I have said, people live by good and bad ones as they live to get good ones and avoid bad ones. Instead of removing the feelings (that is not to say that the Christian doctor ignores treatment), the believer will use them to please God (in all the ways that we have been describing). Removing bad feelings may be impossible this side of heaven. Using them for good is one of the lessons of the Cross. We don't have any better Teacher than our Lord and Savior Jesus Christ.

Being able to administer God's truth to someone in the ways that we have been describing is the only way to set him free (John 8:31-36). Remember that the bondage is to sin (its power) and to sinning (its practice especially as a pattern). Man is a sinner and as a result, he has learned to live by feelings and Satan's lies. In the biblical sense, he is a fool (Proverbs 3:5-8). More specifically, man's bondage is really to self and the constant, though inconsistently practiced, refrain of the

"I wantsies" and living by feelings.

In Romans 6:11-20 and 7:14-25, Paul pictures sin as a power or principle that motivates and drives the sinner, even a saved one. Sin was the believer's master because selfish self was master. Such is the result of God's curse in the Garden. Responding as a getter, even from God, is following Satan's original counsel in the Garden (Genesis 3:1-8). Believers have been rescued from that mindset and lifestyle. The rescue includes freedom from responding sinfully according to Satan's lies and the "I wantsies." Living by feelings and for the "now" to get is replaced by faith working through love (2 Corinthians 5:7). Pleasing God is the saved sinner's goal, but he is in a constant battle between the old self (what he was in Satan's kingdom and family) and the new man (what he is in Christ: 2 Corinthians 5:17; Galatians 5:16-18), and he should thankfully rejoice in God's grace to do so.

Here are two examples that illustrate this freedom (Galatians 5:1-2). One older patient, a believer who lived alone, wanted to avoid surgery on his hip. He was dependent on his family but did not like to acknowledge it. "I don't like being dependent on anyone. I am so used to doing things for myself, even helping others." He was older and had become increasingly sedentary in response to his "predicament in life." He chose that lifestyle thinking that it was better than the alternative. He just didn't want to be bothered with surgery.

Ironically, he said that he had too much to do.

In fact, his issue was not surgery or no surgery, but it was theological. He was in bondage to himself; his self-focus proved that. I asked him two questions: what did he know about grace, and did he love his family. Startled, he said that he was a Christian and that of course he did. He asked me how I could ask such questions. I used that question to address the issue of salvation (and sanctification) by grace alone through faith in action. I defined grace—God's free gift resulting in an actively growing dependence on God. I suggested that perhaps God placed him in his position to acknowledge and act upon that grace. He agreed to "think about it." Then I asked him to tell me the best way that he could show love to his family. He answered, saying "by not being a burden to them." I agreed and asked him to consider how he could be the least burden to them in light of their concerns for his safety. They had asked me how long could he safely stay immobile and not be in danger of falling. Ultimately, he came to understand that putting their concerns ahead of his own was an expression of love. He never repented of his self-centeredness, but I had brought God into the picture using Matthew 22:37-40 and Philippians 2:3-4. I had gone as far as I could; I enjoy pleasing God by taking the care of patients to the highest level: a right relation and reference to God. Those two passages emphasize that the vertical controls the horizontal, and considering others and their concerns over one's own concerns pleases God. The patient had heard an application of the gospel. He consented to the surgery and has been appreciative of the successful surgery and the application of the truth of the Cross in his life.

A second example is the case of a young woman who is a smoker and complains of aches, pains, fatigue, and color change in her hands. She wants to know what is wrong with her and how I will fix it. It is clear that she has one goal: relief from a body that doesn't work the way she wants. She also said, "I don't want to get old." She feared old age, and bodies that don't work are an expression of old age. "That is just not me," she says.

That was an interesting approach to life; it was nothing short of bondage. As is so typical, she was clueless to her bondage. I am not sure what "drove" her. Certainly fear was a main expression of her inner-man problem. She had had this type agenda for decades; she was a driven person and had practiced it well. No matter what I would find in my evaluation, I knew that she had a major theological issue. She was trying to accomplish the impossible. She was tired and weary and did not want hurt (Proverbs 13:15 again!). She could not outrun God's curse on mankind because of sin.

In order to help her, I inquired about this fear—this desire to be healthy that has consumed and colored all of her life. She eventually told me that having a body work like she wants was her way of being in control. She had always "helped." She had taken care of her sisters when their dad left them early in their life. Her mother had to work, and she believed that "being momma" was left to her. She said she was probably bitter. She smoked because it helped her relax. "People tell me to slow down, but I can't." She was willing to dialogue. But there was so much to do in so short a time. I had only begun to scratch the surface. I had opened up a line of communication.

She did agree that she was a "driven person," that she thought she had legitimate reasons for it, and that her driven-ness had not accomplished what she had hoped it would or what it had earlier in her life when she was younger. She told me that she never thought of her way of life as bondage. I asked her to write down her view of life and how applying it in her life had been helpful and hurtful. I also her to read John 8:31-36 and Romans 8:28-29 and tell me how they apply to her. She agreed to do this as well as read the pain papers. Upon leaving, she told me that she appreciated the time spent and the questions asked. They had forced her to think differently. She did not guarantee what she would do, but she would be, and she would think about what we discussed.

The question facing us all is this: are you equipped to help your patient out of the bondage of sinful responses to life? And if you are, how is it going? If not, what do you need to be prepared? The material that I have written, including this book, is designed to help. However, why not consider other avenues of equipping and preparing? Find a local church that has a biblical counseling ministry and get involved. Some of those churches have training programs, which is an excellent resource. Long-distance training, via DVD, is also available. You can contact Redeemer Associate Reformed Presbyterian Church in Duncan-Moore, South Carolina or the Institutes of Theological Studies via the Internet for more information.

As part of trusting and obeying, God expects His physicians to think His thoughts after Him, which includes humble submission to His revealed truth out of joyful thankfulness for being His child. This takes us into the realm of ethics. What is ethics? It is decision making and resultant action or inaction about right and wrong. It is about morality. Living ethically means living by a standard according to a motive with a goal in mind. Biblically, ethics is applying biblical principles and God's truth in order to make decisions to solve problems in order to please God. God's will is the very definition of good, and His moral demands should drive us to practice ethically-based medicine.

This brings us back to the question that I posed earlier in the book: what is the purpose of practicing medicine? Another way to ask that question is: what does it mean to practice ethically-based medicine? It means acting according to a standard with the correct motive and proper goal. This follows logically from the facts that God thinks and acts according to a standard—His own. Man, God's image bearer, is an ethical being and is to act accordingly too via God's standard. In order for us to answer the questions posed, we must know what it is that God wants in terms of our ethical behavior and thinking.

We have heard it said many times: physician, first do no harm.[48] Interesting phrase, and one that I suspect has influenced, maybe controlled, many physicians in their practice. However, what does it mean? It sounds very similar to the idea of "not forcing" my religion (worldview) on my patients. The basic Hippocratic belief is rooted in paganism: nature is the source of healing, and the job of the physician is to aid nature in the healing process. Even in ancient Greece, physicians had many potions and pills to cure ailments; Hippocrates resisted interventionistic medicine, and his treatment recommendations often involved diet, exercise, and wine—all designed to "strengthen" natural forces in recovery. If Nature will cure, then the job of the physician is to hasten Nature's work carefully,

---

48   The phrase "Primum non nocere" (first do no harm) is not found in the Hippocratic Oath itself (when translated from the original Greek), but it is found in the Hippocratic corpus. The Oath does state: "I will prescribe regimens for the good of my patients according to my ability and my judgment and never do harm to anyone."

and at all costs to avoid adding to the burden of illness.

Where does that leave us today? What does it mean to do no harm? Certainly, as Christians, God is sovereign, not nature. The natural order, nature, is a product of God's creation. I suspect that Hippocrates, because of God's creational design and not his desire to seek and honor the God of nature, knew that he was small and that something supernatural must exist. As an unbeliever, he did the best he could. Do no harm meant not to "interfere" with the powers that be. He did believe in non-biblical determinism. Therefore, he was at the mercy of his own logic, the gods, and nature. Again we are back at modern medicine's roots with all its baggage.

All activity in and out of the office that is God-honoring will be motivated by love of God in order to glorify Him with the goal of pleasing Him according to His standard— His Word (Matthew 22:37-40; 2 Corinthians 5:9 and Matthew 6:33; Psalm 19:14). When we speak of ethics in medicine, what comes to mind? Most ethics classes and courses address very important issues regarding "whens" and "whys;" should we prolong life or prolong death by doing or not doing, such as resuscitation, placing the patient on a ventilator, or inserting a feeding tube? The whole area of death and dying is affected by what one believes the purpose of medicine to be. Other common ethical areas include the action of a colleague judged by a board of peers as competent or "inappropriate," the moral-legal issues of compensation from pharmaceutical companies, and the legality of purchasing organ transplants. The question seems to be: is it ethical or unethical to do such and such or to not do it? However, one of the problems is that no standard has been set by which to determine right or wrong. Relativism (relative truth), subjectivity, and a solely horizontal reference to life hold sway in making these important ethical decisions. For you and me as Christians, our standard is set: it is the Word of God. We do need help in sorting God's Word from a person's interpretation of it. But since the practice of medicine involves ethics, practicing is a theological activity.

In the ethics class I recently attended, I learned a great deal and benefited from the teaching and challenges. However, something was missing. The issue regarding the ethics of using (or not using) biblical principles in the care of a patient was never considered. From the examples given so far (and those that follow), I have established that patients who come to you with physical problems are engaged in a theological activity. Furthermore, how they respond to your help is a theological activity. As we have established (I didn't—God did), neutrality is a dangerous myth. However, the mantra, even among some Christian physicians, is to avoid mixing medicine and religion. And yet as we have seen, that statement is a theological misstatement—all are deeply religious, and neutrality is impossible and hides a rebellious spirit toward God. In this book, I am addressing "good" ethics from a different perspective. I presuppose, based on God's Word, that patients, especially struggling ones, need God's truth. Further, I believe Scripture teaches that for a Christian physician to withhold that truth, especially to a believer, that he himself has been given so generously, is "unhelpful," even harmful, and even unethical (2 Corinthians 8:9; 9:8).

As I have said, it seems that most physicians who are Christians seem aware that being a Christian influences their practice of medicine. Yet, I wonder if that fact includes the priority of bringing biblical principles to bear on the patient (as a whole person)—in his care and in that way modeling the great Physician.

In summary, I believe that as you learn and apply these and other biblical truths, you will grow personally, and you will look forward with godly anticipation to using your position to present and administer God's truth to your patient. The concept of biblical "one anothering" is God's requirement for all of God's people everywhere, including those who work in a medical office (John 13:34-35; Acts 6:1-4; 1 John 4:7-12).49 Biblical one anothering involves biblical love—giving, to meet a real need, no matter the cost, with the right motivation (John 3:16; Galatians 2:20; Ephesians 5:2,25; 1 Corinthians 13:3).

49   See page 51 and footnote 24

Administering biblical truth in the most appropriate manner for God's glory and the patient's benefit is both a mandate and a blessing. In fact, the best thing that any patient can do for his health is to know that God is for the body and has given guidelines on how best to care for it (Proverbs 3:5-8). And the best thing any Christian physician can do is to help his patient honor God as a good theologian-steward.

CHAPTER 5

Putting It All Together

WE HAVE COME TO THE place where "the rubber meets the road." It is time to make good on the promises that I have made throughout the book. The issue before us now is how to help the Christian physician to engage in the practice of medicine with a proper vertical reference. How will that look in your daily practice? So far, I have given a rationale for practicing medicine from a biblical perspective, and I have given numerous examples to illustrate certain points. These snippets addressed the "what" and the "how" of practicing medicine as a Christian. Now, I present several more detailed patient scenarios that more clearly illustrate what I have been saying. It is in this way that I am keeping my promises.

Consider the case of any patient with known and provable pathology. I have chosen to present patients with diabetes, hypertension, RA, and breast cancer. These diseases are common and tend to have a chronic nature. Also in the diagnosis and treatment of them, it is easy for the physician to function purely as a "body mechanic." Here, the Medical Model of disease is at its best with proven pathology and proven treatment options.

Making a proper biblically-directed diagnosis and developing a God-honoring treatment plan are musts for Christian physicians. Using their God-given skills competently, but always with a proper vertical reference, honors God and is most beneficial for the patient. In this way he acknowledges his God and reverences Him in a way that reflects well the name of Christ. But as we have said repeatedly, there is more to being a Christian physician.

By way of introduction of this section, consider what is well-known to every physician: the term "functional overlay" or "symptom expression." It is used to describe patients and their complaints as part of their medical problem. In order to truly help the patient, I must think biblically about him and his complaints. In doing so, I have found that I must re-define such medical terms as "functional overlay" and "symptom expression." In fact, these terms are often descriptive indicators of how the patient has and is responding to life in general and to his particular body problem. It is in that light that I have labored to encourage you in the practice of medicine to have a biblical view of man that necessitates a change from a psychosomatic mindset to a spiritual-physiological one (see pages 16-17). The latter term more clearly depicts man as God does in His Word. Remember that it is when you and I understand man as given in the Bible that we can administer God's truth to the whole person. The patient comes to you for help, most of the time for relief, and he wants it in the physical realm. The goal should not be simply "to make a physical diagnosis." From God's perspective, it is for you and me to turn to a God-honoring diagnosis and solution. You will minister to the whole person irrespective of the body problem, and in some cases, because of the body problem.

Let's begin with patients who have diabetes and hypertension. For the most part, the diagnosis is straightforward. Objective data are available for making the diagnosis, and appropriate and effective therapy is at the ready. In these cases, it is easy to focus on data and the tendency is to treat the problem, not the patient. Medications tend to be the mainstay of treatment, but "lifestyle" changes are considered to be an effective therapeutic intervention.

Knowing the full spectrum of the disease—its pathogenesis and pathophysiology, its "natural" history, and treatment algorithm—is mandatory if the physician desires to practice medicine in a God-honoring way. Moreover, the Christian physician can never divorce the physical from the spiritual; he is not to neglect it or fail to consider the influence of one on the other. How would ministering as a Christian physician look when caring for such a patient with a seemingly pure "physical" problem?

First, remember that his physical problem is not simply a "physical" problem. At some point in your treatment, you must convey that truth to him. The question is when and how. That depends on a number of issues that include your relationship to God, your confidence in biblical truth and presenting it to patients, and your relationship with the patient. Biblically, a non-negotiable truth for the believer is that the care of his body is a reflection of his vertical reference to life. It is an outworking of his relationship with Christ. Do you as a Christian physician simply gather data, prescribe medication, and send him on his way to return for a recheck at a follow-up visit? I hope not. Remember that the person is an image bearer of God and has been entrusted with his body. And you have been entrusted with helping him care for it—God's way. So what do you do?

For starters, get to know your patient. The fact that he is your patient means that you already have a relationship with him. What do you do as a result of that relationship? All physicians gather data in a variety of ways: verbally as you interview the patient, written forms especially with new patients, and other reading materials and questionnaires that you have developed for your particular practice and specialty.[50] As you take his history, you learn things by asking questions. In your data gathering, you will move from simply recording physical symptoms, and maybe signs, filling out the data for the EMR (electronic medical record) to learning his expectations, hopes, fears, doubts, wants, and motivation.

As an example, I ask people how life is going in general and also in particular. I generally ask new patients how I can help and what they expect from me. Depending on the answers received, I may be able to detect their concerns, frustrations, and problem areas. I look for and may even probe for information about their church going and their prayer time. Patients are usually ready to answer even if they are not going to church or praying. Depending on the answers, I will ask them about any connection between their feelings (usually

---

50   See pages 102 and 110: In my practice, I developed what I call "pain papers." Actually, they are a series of papers moving from symptoms to information addressing the different types of rheumatic problems to thinking, feeling, and doing. They form a unit and include much information about arthritis and rheumatism in such a manner that patients are confident that "I know rheumatology." Included are discussions on stewardship, stress, circumstances, depression, and "positive thinking." They are designed to give me an opportunity to present biblical truth. For more information or to obtain copies, you can contact me at jimhalla@yahoo.com or consult my book: "Pain the Plight of Fallen Man."

bad ones but also good ones) and their wanting (expectations, hopes, fears), thinking (about life, their problems, and their body), and doing (or not doing). No matter the symptom or the sign, I want to know what makes it worse and what makes it better and their response in hard and good times.

The patient's elevated blood pressure may be due to his disease or could be related to a wrong view and response to life. The Christian physician will evaluate the patient through a spiritual-physiological grid (what symptoms are generated by responses to life situations, so- called "stress"). Similarly, the patient's elevated blood sugar may be related to worsening control of his disease from whatever cause, including non-compliance. His peculiar feelings and behavior may be related to either hyperglycemia or hypoglycemia. Thinking biblically (from the inside out, knowing that feelings are a function of wants, often unmet, and beliefs) will help you investigate which is the cart and which is the horse: did the patient's unbiblical responses to life, even to his failing body, produce poor diabetic control, or did his poor diabetic control produce bad feelings and maybe thinking, or is it a combination of the two? No matter which, you will address both. Ask the patient to honestly examine himself for any unrepentant sin in his life or recurring sinful response pattern. For t his, I like to have the spouse with the patient. Often, two heads are better than one.

Eventually, I want to ask the patient about his relationship with Christ. I may not be able to obtain all the information on this subject in one visit, but I do plant the seed for biblical truth. I may ask him if he is a believer and what that means to him, especially with the body he has. I may ask him what biblical truth he believes applies to him in his situation. I often give him some reading material. For instance, often in my practice, I hear many stories of pain, pain, and more pain, which is often associated with complaints of fatigue. I ask patients what is going on, and many times they tell me that they are overwhelmed, "under the circumstances," and in bondage. Patients especially relate to the concept of being trapped—in bondage. Some may say that they are in a "black hole." They believe that there is no way out. They tell me that having this body, these medications, these exercises to do, this food to eat or not eat is more than they can bear—or in some instances, more than they should have to bear. I am quick to agree with their assessment in the sense that, from their vantage point, "life is the pits." However, I depart from them in regard to their solution. I will say something like: "wow, what a mess. You are in bondage. What you need is truth." It is interesting how many patients agree with that assessment. That opens the door, even slightly, for me to present John 8:31-36:

> To the Jews who had believed in him, Jesus said, "If
> you hold to my teaching you are really my disciples.

> *Then you know the truth and the truth will set*
> *you free. They answered him, "We are Abraham's*
> *descendants and have never been slaves of anyone.*
> *How can you say that we shall be free?" Jesus replied,*
> *"I tell you the truth that anyone who sins is a slave*
> *to sin. Now a slave has no permanent place in the*
> *family, but a son belongs to it forever. So if the Son*
> *sets you free, you will be free indeed.*
>
> (John 8:31–36)

I ask them to read the verses at home and write down three ways those verses help them change their view of life and any results that brings. Some may complain, saying something like this: what does truth have to do with my body problem? I tell them that I am glad they asked. I ask them to explain their way of thinking and addressing their body problem and what their results have been. They often tell me that when they get upset or frustrated, their blood pressure or their sugar acts up. The door is open a little wider for me to be in a position to have patients agree that they have more than a body problem and that their thinking and wanting is detrimental to good health. I am a little closer to bringing biblical principles to bear directly on the person and his care.

When you are gathering data in this manner with the proper motive, you are functioning and hopefully growing as an "inside-out" type of physician. Jesus knew these things inherently, but we don't—so we ask. You want to know how the patient has been handling life in general, and specifically his body problem. You will want to gather more information on his relationship with God in Christ and others, and how that relationship is an asset or a hindrance to him—and to you as his physician. The key is to help him acknowledge and act upon the fact that his relationship with Christ is not just for Sunday or for getting relief from his physical problem. Rather, it is life-changing everywhere: at work, at home, and in the office. And it is to be the reason for him to function as a good steward-theologian. So help him acknowledge that when he takes his medication for blood pressure and diabetes out of gratitude for his salvation and for providing tools to take of his body, he is honoring God. In essence, it is an act of worship (Romans 12:1-2).

At this juncture, you may encounter patients with all types of theological issues that need to be addressed either by you or his pastor (remember the caveat about which kind). They include:

- God's control: is God trustworthy? "I have no business having a body like this. I can't trust the kind of God that would allow it. It was fine for Him to put Jesus on the cross, but it is not fine for Him to treat me this way."
- Salvation is my redemptive right for healing: "Since

Jesus died for me—He was wounded and took my infirmities—I deserve to have healing now." They may point to such verses as Matthew 8:16-17 (Isaiah 53:4-6) for support.

When evening came, many who were demon-possessed were brought to him and he drove out the spirits with a word and healed all the sick. This was to fulfill what was spoken through the prophet Isaiah: He took up our infirmities and carried away our diseases.

(Matthew 8:16-17)

- God is a debtor God who can be manipulated by such things as prayer: "I prayed and am still praying, waiting to be healed. In the meantime, give me something so I can handle my 'bad' body."
- God's love: "If He is so good, why me, and why am I like this?"

These statements and questions express theological issues of top priority. They may not be spoken outwardly by your patient, but many patients—even churchgoers—with chronic diseases, harbor such thoughts and will counsel themselves wrongly. You know that healing, or at least improvement in the patient's medical condition, will probably never come until these issues are successfully addressed. I know that they need to be. The question is when and how. I know that no amount of medication will address them and certainly not God's way. That job is for you to do, Christian physician. Do you dare shirk your responsibility to God and your patients by not taking responsibility for such help?

All of these things and much more are circulating in your mind. In the final analysis, you should ask yourself, "What biblical truth does this patient need first and most in order to help him honor God as His patient?"

- Consider John 8:31-36. We went over these verses earlier. Bondage and freedom are two recurring themes of patients that I encounter in my practice. Contrary to common thinking, the bondage that people "feel" and focus on is not simply related to chronic diseases. Other things are going on and get mixed in with the medical problem. Sometimes the bondage is complicated by problems within a marriage or work and the patient's response to them. It is so important to define the patient's bondage and to help him acknowledge that he is no victim, especially if he is a child of God.

I ask him to list his responses to his problems, including his body problem, and what he has accomplished with them. Many patients tell me that "getting upset" aggravates their problem (Proverbs 3:5-8; 13:15). They have confirmed the biblical truth that handling life properly or improperly has physical ramifications. We have at least one point on our agenda that needs to be addressed if we want to help our patient. Often times this is a hope-engendering discovery for the patient. Most patients have never thought this way about life. At other times, patients simply don't want to take the time nor expend the effort to reorient and reprogram themselves. They would rather rely on anything else than God's truth to bring about change.

Unbiblical thinking about God and self produces hurting bodies. Yet, that is not to say that every hurting and failing body is the result of sinful responses to life. Nor does it mean that sinful responses to life are always accompanied by body problems. I do remind the patient that many unbelievers never come to the office and certainly seem to have fewer physical problems than some Christians. I mention that many smokers and obese people don't seem to have medical problems. I use the illustration that a person could walk across a busy street with his eyes closed and not get hit. But eventually poor stewardship has its own consequences (Proverbs 13:15). Similarly, I emphasize that wrong thinking about and responses to life, self, one's body, and God eventually affect one's body. Christian physicians are like "inside-out" detectives: in addressing the patient, it is important to get to know him as a whole person—thoughts, fears, motivations, and expectations. When these are unearthed—and it may be over several patient visits—I will have him ready to revisit them according to the verses that follow.

- The patient needs to have biblical truth at his disposal. I ask him to write down the followings verses and reflect on them five times per day and record the results: 2 Corinthians 5:9 ("So we make it our goal to please him, whether we are at home in the body or away from it") and Colossians 3:17 ("And whatever you do, whether in word or deed, do it all in the name of the Lord Jesus, giving thanks to God the Father through him"). These verses teach that the believer's goal in all of life, including his physical problem, is to honor God by pleasing Him. Many patients don't know what that means let alone how to do it. That takes us to specific instructions as given above.

- In order to help him function according to 2 Corinthians 5:9, I might ask him to read, recite, and meditate on 2 Corinthians 5:9, 1 Corinthians 6:19-20, and Philippians 4:13 at least five times per day, beginning when he first awakens and ending when he closes his eyes to sleep. The application of those verses can take many forms. For instance, he may not want to get out of bed, let alone take his medications, do his exercises, get up and get busy, or go to work. Focusing on pleasing God, who is pleasable, and His grace for doing so should motivate the believer to get busy doing the very thing he was designed to do—honor God as a steward-theologian.

The goal is to bring the patient face to face with the truth of the living God, the Owner and Designer of his body. For the believer, that fact should change his focus. Armed with these truths and the motivation to please God, he follows doctor's orders by taking his medications, disciplining himself at the table and away from it, exercises and follows his diet as part of good stewardship, and rejoices when he does. These are what I call "yahoos"—God's grace is alive as well! Each of those activities is a time for him to record his thinking, wanting, and response as a result of what I call "biblically-controlled thinking."

When it seems impossible to go on, pleasing God by actively, willfully, cognitively, and purposefully calling to mind His truth by simple recitation or reading of the verse should motivate the believer to be a good steward-theologian. He recalls the gift of the indwelling Holy Spirit and a Savior who bled and died for him. Armed with those facts, he obediently takes care of his body God's way, as evidenced by a growing thankfulness for his new perspective on life. As a child of God, he begins to function as a capable steward, knowing full well it is because of God's grace and his union with Christ. This mindset leads to contentment and simplicity—relief, in life. Desiring and getting relief, which he may never accomplish, will become less important than pleasing God, which is always possible.

- The patient must become a good listener and implementer of what you say. If he is not, then you must help him do so. Many patients are in the "tell-it-to-the doctor" mode or say that "I am just being honest" when they have failed to comply with various doctor recommendations. Often, these statements are justification for poor stewardship. Sometimes patients simply want to talk as if talking is, and is conducive to, good stewardship. Rather, talking is what they do at home as well. Sometimes I have patients repeat what I have said and summarize the salient points of our discussion. And sometimes I use the word "whoa." It is a nice word that I use to redirect the patient who is talking and not listening. Even then, some patients just don't listen well. Listening and properly implementing what has been said are marks of a good theologian-steward.

Let me qualify. That is not to say that the patient is to have a "whatever-you-say-doctor" mentality. In that situation, he may be abdicating his responsibility to honor God as His kind of patient. On the other hand, there is the patient who demands certain information and medications, knows "a lot of things," and compares and contrasts what you say with what others say—including what the Internet says. Neither approach by the patient is necessarily God-honoring. Help the patient stay balanced. One way I do that is by telling the patient that he doesn't have to agree with me. Similarly, I tell him that I may not agree with him. But one of my goals is to have him know that I have heard him and understood him correctly. And another is that he has heard and understood me too. So I ask him to hear me. If we disagree, it is not out of misunderstanding or ignorance. Especially when interviewing a new patient with whom I am beginning to build a relationship, I encourage the patient to ask as many questions as he thinks are needed in order to fulfill his proper role as theologian-steward.

I don't mind if he asks questions about information from various sources, but in the end I want him to remember that I am the doctor that God, in His providence, has put in his life at that time, and that he is the patient that God has placed in my life at that time. He might not agree with my assessment, but I want him to know how I arrived at it.

- When it comes to medication, antihypertensive and diabetic medications become tools to be used to honor God. Non-compliance should not be a problem. But if and when it is, that fact provides opportunities for future discussions of his relationship to God and its impact on the patient's lack of Godly stewardship.

- Certainly, it is Christlike to be a caring and comprehensive physician with the desire to please God, being thankful for your salvation (remember, the unbelieving physician can never approach anyone or his problem with a correct vertical reference to life. He will not correctly minister to the whole person). You may recommend so-called lifestyle changes that may include regular exercise, weight loss, appropriate eating habits, and even a change in the food he eats and how he eats. Help the patient be honest in his self inventory, repent in areas that he has sinned against God, and in response, help him put on Holy-Spirit-directed self control (Galatians 5:23). I have two handouts that I give when I discuss the issue of sin, forgiveness, and repentance. I have found these very effective when addressing this misunderstood subject. The patient needs clear teaching on the subject in order to promote proper application.[51]

When the subject of "lifestyle changes" is raised, it is a

---

51   The issue of repentance seems to be a recurring theme in patient care. The usual Greek word translated *repentance* is *metanoia* which means "a change of mind, changed thinking, and a rethinking." The change is one from the old way thinking to a new thinking – God's way. Thinking changes and confession of sin follows (confession is essentially agreement – with God). Sin is exposed, confession follows, and the person with his new attitude puts on a different kind of action or conduct. You will see this dynamic played over and over again. See footnotes 20 and 31, pages 47 and 57.

perfect opportunity to broach the subject of self control. It is a fruit of the Spirit. Every believer is to be growing in that area. However, the development of self control is not instantaneous. In fact, the Bible is plain how it comes (1 Timothy 4:7-8:"…rather train yourself to be godly. For physical training is of some value, but godliness has value for all things, holding promise for both the present life and life to come"). The verse teaches that you must discipline yourself for the purpose of godliness; there is no other option. Godliness for your patient is being a good steward of his body. In its essence, biblical discipline is the continued daily effort in training yourself to choose pleasing God rather than self in order to reflect your Savior. That comes as the patient denies the self within by doing what God wants him to do. In your patient's case, it is functioning as God's kind of patient.

How would implementing the principles presented above "look" in your office, given the time constraints and the patient's interest in being God's kind of patient? Consider this summary composite-patient encounter (I will call her Ms. B):

> Doctor:"Ms. B, your blood pressure is good, but your hemoglobin A1C is out of range. Tell me about it."
>
> Ms. B:"I have been very busy, things to do and things on my mind."
>
> Doctor: "Those are important issues, I assume, but

what do they have to do with you honoring God with your body? Have you neglected the truths that we discussed at your last visit?"

Ms. B: "I guess I put them on the back-burner—I guess I am saying I think that it just wasn't that important."

Doctor: "And what have been the results?"

Ms. B: "Probably that I made things worse, or at least I have been hard on my body."

Doctor: "Do you remember what we have talked about in regard to your body and 1 Corinthians 6:19-20?"

Ms. B: "Yes. My body is God's property on loan to me because of the Holy Spirit. It is so easy to forget that—especially when things are hectic."

Doctor: "Right, I do understand that. I wonder what makes it easy to 'forget' that truth. And how can I help you not only to remember that truth, but for it to impact your life?"

Ms. B: "I am not sure – some of that, I must do myself."

Doctor: "That is an important step—taking personal responsibility. If you would like, I can give you some suggestions. However, do you think that a first step is repenting of failure to do so? I will be happy to spend some time later discussing this with you, or you may want to

talk with your pastor. I will be happy to discuss it with
him if he would like. In addition, why not consider reading this booklet that discusses 1 Timothy 4:7-8 and doing
the assignments in it? When you come back for your next
visit, I will revisit your use of 1 Corinthians 6:19-20 and
2 Corinthians 5:9. I will be looking forward to hearing
how your life has improved as a result of being God's
kind of patient. Let's pray."

And we did!

The above is just one method of approaching patients as
a whole person. The above scenario was shortened and may
have seemed harsh or behavior driven. In "real-life," I would
wait for answers to the questions posed. Any question worth
asking is worth being answered. My goal was to relate to her,
in her world, in her situation. I reminded Ms. B of her proper
motivation as a child of God (2 Corinthians 5:9). Second,
when she was faced with giving in to feelings, functionally
she jettisoned her only true help. Failing to please God only
worsened her situation. Repentance was in order, but she
may or may not be with me at that point. But I—as well as
you—shouldn't disregard repentance. I offered to help her
understand what repentance is and its importance. Understanding the subject of repentance and its importance in all
of life may take time to develop. I encouraged her to get in-

volved in her local church, but I would like to know what she had been taught.[52] Third, by God's grace, she acknowledged that she had "not done a good job" (maybe not repentance, but patients don't always say what she said, let alone repent!). Fourth, I counseled her to counsel herself by applying specific biblical principles. Fifth, I gave her an assignment specifically designed for her that addressed her problem, and I gave her hope by giving her a return visit and the promise of following up on her progress. At follow-up, I must be sure I do so! And I must ask about repentance. If she fails to repent, I must decide if what I did was all for nothing or whether she needs more help and hope.

Since she seems to desire to honor God in her body, and since she seems to have repented of failing to implement changes in her thinking, wanting, and doing, she is encouraged to view the needed physical changes as an extension of who she is in Christ. Therefore, these changes that we suggest will not be drudgery or a forced requirement, but reminders that

---

52   Several times I mentioned having the patient connect to her local church and her pastor or other church leaders. There is a caveat. You need to know something about the pastor. Is he knowledgeable about the application of biblical principles in patient care? Is he willing and able to help you help his sheep and your patient be God's kind of patient? These are important issues because a pastor not committed to the truth of Scripture can do more harm than good.

her God loves her as His child and deserves to be honored. They are part of God's sovereign control that is meant for her good. With that focus the patient—we hope—will direct her attention to developing Christlikeness, using unpleasantness to do so. On return, she may say something like this:

> "I have taken my medications, done my exercises, and changed not only my eating habits to lose weight but to honor God. I did not think that I could, and sometimes I didn't want to, but I remembered that God is good and powerful. The Cross proves it, and life is better for me and my family when I live as a good steward-theologian."

I am not saying that this full scenario will play out daily. In fact, the truth of the matter is that most patients resist the application of biblical truth in their medical care except to get healing. It may be that they are not Christians (Romans 8:8). Or it may be because they are Christians functioning as unbelievers. They may be poorly taught as to the "what" and "how" of progressive sanctification. One of the privileges and responsibilities of the Christian physician is to minister as a God pleaser no matter the results. So be encouraged as you do your part properly!

As you ask questions, patients (even believers) may introduce various symptoms and report pressures and "stress" in their lives. Knowing from the Bible that people are "inside-outside" people, you know that the term "stress" tells you something about their thinking and its foundation—it is steeped in a victim mentality—"something outside of me is making me to feel and act a certain way." The responsibility issue, as we have seen, is a major characteristic of biblical stewardship and will need to be addressed early on in their care if they are going to succeed in honoring God with their bodies. They must come to see that the real problem is how they handle "outside" issues, biblically or otherwise.

As Christian physicians who are not to be "physical mechanics," we do treat the physical, and we must encourage our patients to do likewise. That brings us to consider how "outside-of-you" problems "cause" you to think and feel a certain way. Simply said—they can't. That which is outside of a person is the stage, situation, or stimulus in which the person expresses his thinking and wanting. A phone call from the Internal Revenue Service is neutral in and of itself. What you think it means determines your response to it. If a person perceives hard times, such as an audit or request to return overpayment, he may well be fearful and worry. As we have noted, these proceed from the inner man—his heart. They are a manifestation of interpreting the events in life based on wanting and thinking. One's interpretative grid may be his logic, feelings, or experience, or it is biblical principles. The former leads to wrong responses that actually produce more body problems. And the latter leads to a God-honoring response which should lead to contentment, even in the midst of trouble. Usually, no one wants a call from the IRS—too much grief and heartache. However, if the caller announces a refund, then relief, joy, and thanksgiving follow—a so-called positive response; if an audit is announced, then worry, fear, and even anger often occur. Why? Nothing touched the responder from the outside. Everything occurred inside. The person's thinking and wanting elicits fear and worry or joy and thanksgiving in response to pressures of life. Those responses reflect a person's vertical orientation to life (where God is in his thinking) that in turn determine its horizontal expression.

The same line of reasoning (which is biblically-derived but unknown or rejected by the secular community) is helpful in understanding patients who have bodies that they don't like. Truly, medical problems are burdens. They can change plans, the manner and mode of doing things, and how one spends his money and time. And yet, the real problem is not the deteriorating body (2 Corinthians 4:16-18). God has not chosen to reverse the effects of His curse on sin in this life. Thus, bodies deteriorate. By God's grace, the believer can function as a God-pleaser, using his body to do so even during its deterioration.[53] Therefore the key is the believer's response to his

---

53   See my booklet: "What to do When Your Body Fails You": via Timeless Texts or Redeemer Presbyterian Bookstore, Moore SC

failing body. Helping patients know and apply these biblical principles is an important, indeed vital, part of functioning as a Christian physician.

The Christian doctor must be very careful, because he too may fall into the trap of concluding that wanting, thinking, feeling, and doing are unrelated to physical ailments or that medications are the answer. If that is the case, he may assume that symptoms are due to "stress." Usually by *stress* a person means that something *outside* of him is *doing* "it" to him. People, when explaining what they mean by the word *stress* (pressure), say that "it is a person (spouse/boss/enemy/ etc.) or situation (my marriage/body/illness) that causes my problem." Another patient may say that stress is that which is *in* him as a result of being in the situation. He may say that he feels tight and nervous inside, that his chest hurts, or that he has abdominal pain. Medicine has various *(mis)labels* for these conditions such as irritable bowel syndrome, tension headaches, panic attacks, situational depression, and even fibromyalgia—I call them "response-to-life" conditions—that either cause or complicate the body problem. While the labels may describe some type of physiological response, they do not identify the spiritual-physiological significance of the inner responses of the person to his situation. The above thinking is not intended to minimize a person's troubles that God has providentially brought into his life. There really is something

outside. What I am talking about is not to deny, or even un-
derrate, that troubling and difficult time. What I am emphasizing is that the person's response to the "something outside"
is the key. In that way, I maximize God's grace.

At this point, I ask the patient the direct question: "How
can something outside of you cause you to feel and think a
certain way?" Most have not thought the issue through. And
I have yet to hear a patient answer the question from a biblical perspective. That is one reason why I have written this
book. Both the patient and the doctor may assume that the
problem is "outside" of the patient and fail to consider that
the patient's response is related to his thinking and wanting (his worldview and presuppositions about life, God, and
himself) which, as we know, are inner-man activities. Doctor
and patient may think symptoms "need" to be treated. After
all, his diabetes and hypertension need to be controlled, and
stress, we are told, is "bad for your health." When his physical problems of hypertension and diabetes and their control
color all else, that coloring impacts all else. Then his worldview comes into play. Does the Bible and what it says about
man and life inform the Christian, or do science (however
defined) and medicine with a different view of man and his
problems trump Scripture? That question is not esoteric or
merely academic but practical. You and I deal with it whether
we recognize it or not, and daily the answer we give impacts

how we function as Christian physicians. The Bible says that outside pressure is part of a fallen world, and it is needed for growth and maturing in Christlikeness (Romans 5:1-5; James 1:2-4,12; 1 Peter 1:6-7—these verses teach it is not the pressure that is key but the proper response to it).

- It is here that more information is needed from the patient. This requires time for more questions. It is here that the Christian physician has to restrain himself— it is so easy to justify a pill in lieu of presenting biblical truth. Instead, ask your patient motivation-type questions such as: "Tell me what happens when you become frustrated. What do you think? What do you want? When you don't get it, what happens?" Ask him to explain to you why he responds to the same situation differently some days contrasted to other days. Help the patient understand that it is his response that is a motivation issue—an inside/out issue involving his thinking and wanting. This is a major "therapeutic" maneuver. When his thinking and wanting don't please God, his response will reflect his displeasure at God's providence. When that happens, his body will suffer, and God will not be honored. Applying God's answers, beginning with his motivation for life, will help him to function as God's kind of patient. And the truth appropriate for the patient can only come if proper data are gathered.

- Sometimes patients will be reluctant to hear, let alone apply, biblical truth. In those cases the Christian physician should do a self inventory, asking the following questions of himself: do I know my patient? Have I ministered to the physical aspect as God would have me? Does the patient know that I am committed to helping him God's way for God's glory and his benefit? Have I heard him, and have I given him the most appropriate biblical truth in the most appropriate way that I can? Is there a Godly person such as his pastor who is committed to bringing God's truth to bear in his life to whom I may refer him? Do I have the desire and knowledge to counsel him myself—say, after hours or during lunch? If you have considered any of these, praise God! You are on the right path. If you have done or are doing the right thing, you can know that you pleased God, no matter what the patient chose to do. You are not responsible for the results of your efforts – only for the message and the manner of its presentation.

- As I mentioned earlier, when the patient returns for follow-up visits, you remember that he is a Christian and that you presented 1 Corinthians 6:19-20 to him as seminal verses to help him be God's kind of patient. Therefore, not answering for him, not only will you ask him if he is taking his medications, losing weight, and exercising, you will ask him his motivation for doing so. You will want to know if he is applying the verses and why, how he is applying them, and how those verses have been a blessing to him daily. You are ministering to the whole person. Praise God.

Perhaps the patient is a non-believer. How do you engage him? Do you simply function as a "body mechanic" or as a "spiritual mechanic" by simply evangelizing him? This can be tricky because the patient may say "no religion stuff" or "my thinking and wanting isn't the problem—it is my body that hurts, so fix it!" The important principles are:

- First, he came to you for body help and he thinks outward treatment of the body is all that he needs. His focus is solely on relief and his way. He may not say it that way, but that is his agenda.

- Second, the goal is not to argue with him—it is for you to honor Christ. You do that best by speaking truth. You may have to say something such as this: "your diabetes and blood pressure will be hard to treat. We can use more medications, but those won't do the job entirely. It is up to you to respond correctly."

- Third, bring some biblical truth into the picture gently, yet appropriately, whenever you can. For instance, have him challenge his own logic. "Everything is fine, you say. What do you base your conclusion on—especially since your hemoglobin A1C is 10, you have gained weight, and you are not taking your medications properly?" Wait for his answer. You know Proverbs 13:15 ("Good understanding wins favor, but the way of the unfaithful is hard"), but he doesn't. Until he is ready to say that his way is not working, he will resist biblical truth.

Certainly God's promises are not applicable for the unbeliever as they are to God's people. The unbeliever is on the "wrong side of the fence." He is not in a position to receive God's truth and His blessings. However, because God is gracious, He sends the sun and the rain on the just and unjust (Matthew 5:45). And more so, the Bible describes and prescribes activity and thinking that often leads to improved health, even for the unbeliever. The unbeliever, although never praising or crediting God for His kindness to him, will use these principles of good health. In the end, his refusal to acknowledge and act upon his need for God and a proper relationship to Him through Christ will cause the greatest body problem known to man—eternal damnation in the torment of hell.

So what do you do? One way to approach him is to meet him where he is—on the wrong side of the fence. If he is not struggling *in* and *with* life in general and especially in regard to his physical problems, his interest in hearing biblical truth will be minimal or non-existent. This holds for the believer who is functioning as an unbeliever. The resistance is all part of God's providence. Therefore, you will work hard to get to know him. You know that sin has its consequences. He doesn't. But unbelievers will not successfully run from God. So engage him when he is most vulnerable and plant the seeds of truth along the way that may bear fruit during this vulnerability. In his vulnerability, he will accept something, usually something wrong; so why not offer him something good instead? Is that unethical? No, it is unethical *not* to help one who is vulnerable, by God's providence, to you.

In your taking of history (data gathering), you may have discovered that he is having "personal" problems or responses to them that have aggravated his physical problem. Because most patients are clueless to the connection between their bad feelings and their response to life, including their physical problems, you have to teach them. How? One way is to have him tell you about those times and his response in terms of thinking, wanting, and acting. He may acknowledge his problems and at such times be ready to seek help—true help. You may send him out with a gospel tract and pray that he acknowledges the hardness of his life now contrasted with the beauty and joy of salvation and life after salvation. Unless he changes his approach to life, he may consider the gospel tract just another of man's gimmicks. And in all likelihood, his physical improvement will be less than it could be. Fighting

God has consequences in this life as well as the life to come. As a caveat, it is always interesting to me how often God brings seemingly good health to unbelievers and how the unbeliever misuses that gift to his own detriment.

Let's take another scenario—a patient with RA. I am very familiar with this scenario. Again, for the most part, we are dealing with proven disease. Definite and objective criteria have been established for the diagnosis of RA. But it is well known that "functional overlay" (our old "friend"!) plays a major role in the complaints of pain and fatigue, both common symptoms reported by RA patients. Patients usually present with complaints of pain and discomfort and a history of swollen joints. So how would you approach the patient?

- Again, getting to know your patient is crucial. Generally, there are many varied responses to questions concerning the impact or assumed impact of the disease on the patient. Some simply want a diagnosis and treatment "so that it is gone. "Fix it" is the mantra. Other patients don't know what is going on and may be fearful and so concerned that concern has morphed into worry. Others are informed from a variety of sources (family, neighbor, Internet, or television).

Pain and fatigue are twin cousins and major complaints. The mechanical inefficiency of the body as a result of certain medical conditions such as RA makes things harder. Yet attitudinal problems can also produce pain and fatigue, which are linked and can compound each other. All of this leads to failure to do a job or be responsible, which intensifies symptoms (pain and fatigue) but not necessarily the disease.

Some of the "harder to treat or take care of" patients with RA are those who have been healthy and simply have no time for God's providence. A patient may say something along these lines: "I have things to do, I need to get back to my task (for example, to the mission field), and this disease is slowing me down—your job is to fix it." On the other hand, some patients are simply not happy campers because "woe is me." Their attitude is that God let them down, made a mistake, or just isn't aware of what is going on. They are down and even out. The disease is a problem, but what it represents from the patient's perspective looms even larger in terms of helping him respond in a healthy manner, let alone in a God-honoring one.

- Since the patient's focus is on his body, I have to start there. It is amazing how you can simplify the diagnosis and treatment in spite of the plethora of literature that is both patient and physician-directed. That is one of the benefits of being a skilled, qualified physician. Yet some patients seem to resent simplification. They seem to "enjoy" their discomfort. I concentrate on the body problem (in this case RA), but not as a "body mechanic."

- There are always ways to bring God's truth to bear on the patient and his situation, even if the patient is not ready to hear it. For instance, when I speak of pathology and reviewing laboratory results and radiographs with the patient, I bring into the conversation a normally-functioning musculoskeletal system and body, emphasizing the way God initially created it. Moreover, I emphasize thinking and wanting—motivation. Most patients tell me how they handle their disease and unwanted feelings. Common responses are "I live with it," "I grin and bear it," "I use mind over matter and positive thinking," and "I cope." I ask them the results of these responses and what they attribute "pain relief" to. Every time I can, I bring God into the picture. I say something like this: God made you a duplex person so that you should and can control your thinking (I explain "duplex" to them so that the patient knows he is more than body and his thinking affects the physical). I give him some of my patient-designed material. In closing the visit, I often pray with the patient. I am careful to pray, not so much for healing, but for wisdom, courage, and patience for both him and me.

- I may not do all the above in the first visit, but that visit is a most critical one. The initial return appointment for the new patient is also crucial. By that time, the patient has had time to perceive that I care and that I have some knowledge. A trusting relationship takes time to develop but must begin early and is invaluable for effectively presenting God's truth.

- Then, as we worked together, my goal is to utilize that relationship to highlight the patient's relationship to God in Christ. You can do it several ways: "winning your spurs," so to speak, is by you helping him take care of his body. Often patients are hurting. They think: can anybody help? Having active RA (multiple joints with synovitis) takes a toll on one's body and makes focused thinking difficult. When I prescribe an effective or potentially effective drug regimen, the patient's RA improves. In that context, I have "won" the patient's confidence. To him, I am not simply a talker but a doer. Since the "fire" (active synovitis) of his RA is quieted down (or even the potential of it happening), I am in a position to ask him how his relationship with Christ has impacted his life, especially since he has a "broken" or ineffectively functioning body.

- I may even ask him a few "what if" questions: what if there is no cure or relief? What if God says "no" to cure? What if one of the medications that he is fearful of taking is the best choice for treatment? Weaving God into the clinical picture appropriately, gently, and boldly takes time and skill. An example would be something like this: "Can we slow down? I know that you are hurting and that you have RA. I am here to help you—but not simply to fix your body. I can do that fairly easily. I am also greatly interested in helping you think about things differently. You are not the first nor will you be the last one who has something like this. Let's treat the body medically, but *focus* on pleasing God and leave the results to Him. In that way, you will do what is best for your body as He is being honored."

Ministering truth God's way begins with an understanding of the biblical truths presented in this book (certainly not limited to them!) and confidence in their application. Churches and biblical counseling training institutes are available to enrich you in this process. In addition, I give out and ask the patient to read the various handouts that I have mentioned earlier. I developed these materials because I was unable to find appropriate reading material for patients—material that emphasized a Christian approach to giving and receiving medical care. I needed material that emphasized and taught biblical principles with the goal of applying them for God's glory and the benefit of the patient. (See footnotes 8, 24, 27, 40, 50, and pages 102 and 110). You see, I could not return to my former way of treating patients!

Once the diagnosis is made, treatment is usually started.

Some RA patients want everything "right now," and others don't want anything. It is important to learn where the patient is in both instances. One patient drove a long way to see me, thinking that I would tell her that her RA did not need to be treated. She had prayed for God to heal her. He hadn't, but she preferred "waiting on Him" instead of turning to medication, the very gift that God had provided for her that *may* have slowed down or even put her present active disease into remission. I asked her if she was testing God by denying His gift. She thought about it and agreed that she was functioning as a poor theologian-steward and determined that she desired to be a good one. She agreed to take one of the newer biologic agents.

As I have pointed out, it is not easy living with an inefficient, hurting body. It is tiring; it demands time and energy. Simple things are not so simple. Patients may say that they can't sleep, that they are overwhelmed and discouraged by uncertainty and pain, that they are fearful, and (on further questioning) that they are bitter and resentful. One example that I remember vividly is a patient with easily diagnosed and treatable RA who continued to complain of pain and fatigue in spite of the fact that by clinical and laboratory examination, her RA was much improved, maybe in remission. What did I do? As a learner, I gathered further information. She told me she was working two jobs, and she and her husband disagreed about her work schedule. I asked her what made it so important to have two jobs and to live in disagreement with her husband.

What I discovered was that she was convinced that her dad had mistreated her and demeaned her by saying that she would never amount to anything. She was convinced that she would be disabled in ten years from the RA. She was convinced (she said "felt like") that she had a limited time to prove her dad wrong. What drove her was not God's love for her, her love for God, or her love for her family, but *vindication*! Her real problem was not with her dad or her body but with God. She was running from God. God had given her that dad, and she did not like it—in fact, she was bitter and resentful. She had wanted something from her dad that she thought she needed and deserved. The less she got from her dad, the harder she tried to please him to get it. Eventually bitter and disillusioned, she gave up trying. Her dad let her down. Now her body represented an obstacle to reaching her goal of proving Dad wrong.

Her body, her husband, and her family paid the price for this choice and its pursuit. No drugs or medications could correct her whole-body problem. Being a 2 Corinthians 5:9 person was not on her radar screen. It did not interest her. She had her own identity (perceived abuse by Dad) and her own agenda (proving him wrong), and she pursued her agenda with vigor. She was a churchgoer, and I wondered how she thought and even felt Sunday after Sunday, sitting under the preaching of the Word. She did not want to talk about her identity, agenda, or its pursuit. She continued to have inactive disease but many complaints.

When you push all other things aside and remove all the loose ends, the fundamental issue in patients like the one I just described is one of control—"I can't do what I want when I want and I am upset. The uncertainty of life is too burdensome for me. That's why I respond the way I do." That patient had an inordinate desire for approval and acceptance and with it, security and comfort. When, where, and how that developed, I am not sure. In response to what she believed was her dad's failure (perhaps she was abused, but since he wasn't there for me to ask, I don't know. But to help her, I did not need that knowledge) she sought to control her life—to prove her dad wrong and prove herself right. She was going to get approval one way or the other. It didn't matter to her that her goal was wrong (anti-2 Corinthians 5:9), that her family was suffering, and that her response was as sinful as she believed her dad's to be. Moreover, she was competing with God—control is His business, not hers. Our business is to become more like Christ in *and* by the situation (Romans 8:35-37; 1 Corinthians 10:13). Most patients haven't thought about life, let alone their physical problems, from this perspective. Wanting something other than what God wants and seeking to change the circumstances rather than their response is tantamount to complaining about God's providence. Certainly, a father abusing children is sinful and must be dealt with whenever possible. However, her response to that "abuse" is sinful as well (Matthew 7:1-6). In the same way, crying out to God for help and understanding is one thing, but demanding a changed body (or situation or dad) is another (Psalm 4-5, 13).

Seeking control is generally competing with God, which can be expressed in a variety of behaviors and attitudes, usually described by the person in terms of feelings: fear, depression, worry, and even bitterness and resentment. (This is not to say that lack of self-control is not sinful – it is. Seeking to do what God commands is what is needed.) When bad feelings occur, patients invariably report more symptoms and believe that the disease—in this case, RA—is actually worsening when, in fact, that is not the case. In situations like this, it is time to say "whoa" to the patient. It is so easy to move along the party line and medicate both the RA and the "emotional" symptoms that result from wrong thinking and wanting. In neither case are you ministering to the whole person God's way. Even talk therapy, cognitive behavioral therapy, and positive thinking are tools reported to bring relief. And yet the results are almost always less than gratifying; the patient is still himself. The heart of the matter, the person's heart motivations, has not been addressed. Feelings may change with medications, but his response to life, including physical problems, hasn't changed. Why? It is because the Holy Spirit hasn't worked. Only growth in godly sanctification brings about such change.

If you do move along the "party line," then you are functioning as if you and the patient are oblivious to the omnipresent God and His purpose in bringing "all things" to pass for His glory and the good of the person (Romans 8:28-29 and 2 Corinthians 5:9). So ask: Why would God send His Son, who bled and died on the cross for you, and leave you, His child, in the middle of an ocean all alone with no resources? Perish the thought! Contrary to feelings and his experience, the believer is never alone—the Cross proves that fact.

Let's say the patient is tracking with you; he understands and accepts that he has not been God's kind of steward-theologian and that should be his major goal. His focus now is on pleasing God and being His kind of spouse, worker, and parent in the context of his body problem. As a physician, we don't minimize the physical problem, but we remind the believer that his primary goal should not be relief. Rather, there is joy in pleasing God even when his body is not working like he wants and at one time thought he deserved. For our patient, desires had morphed into demands, and when the demands were not fulfilled, he had responded with disappointment and resentment (James 1:13-16; 4:1-3). Now, his thinking has changed as he takes to heart 2 Corinthians 5:9 and Philippians 4:13. He says that he still hurts, but he is functioning as God's kind of patient, which is more important to him than relief.

He has experienced the fact that stewardship actually is best for him, and he is becoming more aware that it is because God designed him to grow in Christlikeness in eternity past (Ephesians 1:4). He has come to realize that applied biblical truth is not a mask or anesthetic for the discomfort that accompanies physical problems. Rather, it is a surpassingly superior way to live and carries with it benefits that only Christians thinking God's thoughts and desiring what God desires are able to appreciate and enjoy. Oh, how I long to have myself, patients, and doctors function with a proper vertical reference and to rejoice how God uses them to advance His kingdom!

In this patient's case, his improved outlook corresponds to an improvement in his physical condition—his RA is coming under control. I wonder if his new approach to life and to his physical problem is due to his improvement or the improvement has contributed to his new outlook. In one sense, it doesn't matter. He has learned and applied valuable truths that will be a blessing in all of life, and if there is improvement, that will contribute to it.

Let's consider another patient scenario: the patient with breast cancer. The diagnosis of cancer often brings shudders throughout one's body. The "C" word is loaded with much freight. Cancer, a common disease, exacts a toll on patient, physician, and the medical system. With diabetes, hypertension, and RA, the diagnosis is relatively easy. Moreover, treatment protocols for many cancers are also very clearly worked out. There is much hustle and bustle in terms of making the diagnosis, orchestrating the various diagnostic and treatment plans and regimens, and receiving specific treatment. Many people are involved in this system of patient care. For your patient, the diagnosis is made and treatment instituted. Now what? Unless there is metastatic disease or some complication from treatment, pain is usually not a major symptom. However, fatigue and discomfort are. What will you do?

- As we have said, it is quite easy to function as a "body mechanic." The cancer patient is now on a solid treatment regimen. What more is there to do? Things may change but as of yet, they haven't. What biblical principles will you bring to the fore to help her respond in a God-pleasing manner?

- The tendency is for her to cope, accept, get by, or tolerate the situation. These are poor and counterfeit alternatives for functioning as a Christian oyster (remember 2 Corinthians 5:9). All types of thoughts may be running through her mind – what next? What now? Will I respond to chemotherapy? Will my hair grow back? Why am I so tired? How can I keep going—I feel so bad?

How can you help her address, answer, and respond to those concerns God's way?

- For one, it is important to be honest about cancer's attack on her body. In addition, receiving chemotherapy is not easy. Her body is being "leaned upon" heavily. Fatigue and bad feelings are part of that deterioration. But let's make sure we are straight on this: bodies decay without any help from any known disease such as cancer, RA, or diabetes (2 Corinthians 4:16-18; Romans 6:23). This phenomenon is commonly called old age or the aging process. It is not natural; it is the result of the curse leveled upon man because of sin (see Genesis 5 and the refrain: "and he died"). Often, people who don't respond to getting older in a proper biblical manner follow the same pattern when faced with *other* body problems. At this point, it is helpful to remind her of what and who she is: as a believer, her identity isn't drawn from her experience—"I am cancer victim" or "I am a cancer survivor." No, she is a child of the loving God, nestled in His arms. She has a true identity; it is in Christ. That is what will sustain her—though not necessarily cure—but the God-given desire and grace to honor Him out of gratitude for the Cross and salvation and the privilege of being His kind of theologian-steward will help her.

- Next, you encourage good stewardship by what she thinks and doesn't think as well as what she does and doesn't do. Help her settle the issue of determinism. Only the Lord knows the end because He has ordained the end (in her case, the results of treatment) as well as the means (in this case, treatment). If God is not the Controller and Sustainer of the entire universe, including her problem, then something else is. What? It can only be chance. How illogical can you be? To assume that all things work out according to chance and luck is sheer irrationalism. How could anyone have hope and confidence with pure chance as her understanding of life? You can't! If God is who He says He is and you are united to Him in Christ by the indwelling Holy Spirit, then the issue of control and determinism are settled in God's—and as a result, your—favor. The fact of God's sovereignty gives you hope and confidence to do what you need to do in order to honor Him regardless of the outcome of treatment.

- Settle the issue of thankfulness (1 Thessalonians 5:18 says, "give thanks in all circumstances, for this is God's will for you in Christ Jesus"). Interesting issue. Only God's grace, the Cross, and God's Word as one's interpretive grid for all circumstances can reorient her to minister to others in her time of need. The thankfulness is not for the cancer, which is another expression of God's curse on man due to Adam's sin, but for the opportunity it provides to rely on God and His grace and minister that grace to others. That is the way of the Cross.

The tendency in all of these "handling-life situations" (the culture tends to call these "emotional problems" and "functional overlay" and label them as a form of a mental disorder) is to use medications. In fact, in these situations, there is nothing wrong with the emotions. They are usually overworking, if anything. The issue is the thinking and wanting in response to God's providence. The person's heart—the site of thinking and wanting—must be trained by biblical truth so that when faced with these situations, he responds according to that truth. Thinking from the inside out, not simply giving medications, is part of practicing biblically-based medicine. As we have pointed out early in the book, the type of education being delivered in our medical schools is not training doctors to practice this type of medicine. Moreover, no one is doing training of doctors in practice now. Therefore, those of us seeing patients now must begin to and continue to practice as God's kind of physician. These issues are inner-man ones and must be answered His way. (Remember, that is where the Holy Spirit dwells and works in the believer and is not influenced by medications but rather by God's grace and truth.)

One last point that applies to all patients is this: please recall the discussion that addresses how something on the outside of a person "causes" or "makes" him have bad feelings. This question is a universal one in the practice of medicine, and it must be answered God's way. I approach the subject this way. Although everyone has an environment, nurture, and a past, these are not determiners of thoughts and desires. Certainly a person is influenced by his past and nurture. But biblically, you are not primarily or ultimately your environment, nurture, or past. If you were, then Jesus would have been the most "emotionally" damaged person in all of history. As Christians we should not (at least knowingly) minimize the hard situations in which people find themselves. Life is tough. All of us have seen patients with multiple medical problems, some of their own making and others not. Linked to God's providence (one's environment, nurture, and past) is His grace which influences a person to change thinking and wanting.

Remember that the believer, a new creature, has radically changed thinking and wanting that are different from the old man (what he was as an unbeliever—2 Corinthians 5:17). It seems easy to ignore or downplay this radical change when faced with hard times. But the believer is able to think and act according to biblical principles in contrast to living by feelings. He can and does recognize the superiority of living as a Psalm 1:1-3 and Proverbs 1:7 person—a wise man.[54] The wise man will use irritations, such as cancer, for that which God purposed them—to become more like Christ out of gratitude for the Cross. Otherwise, even sanctification and growth in Christlikeness can be selfish—when others are not considered and God's honor is not at stake. When there is hurt such as when a knife cuts into the flesh or any other physical problem, the believer will continually train himself to seek after the greater, the greatest, good this side of heaven— Christlikeness. That is grace and the beauty of God.

Now we are ready to again consider the crucial question that we have addressed along the way: how can something on the outside cause certain feelings? As covered earlier, thinking and wanting control attitude and actions. Therefore, it is only through wrong thinking and wanting about the situation, himself, and God that one is controlled by his circumstances. Jesus wasn't, and neither should the Christian

---

54   See Psalm 1:1-3: there are things the wise man doesn't do: walk, stand, and sit under the influence of Satan's lies (these three terms represent a progressive effect). That is why he is wise. As a result, he delights in his God and his teaching, and he is likened to a growing, large productive tree. Situations may not change, but the wise do. The wise man is one who fears the Lord, which is the dominating awareness of who God is and rightfully has something to say about the person's every thought, desire, and action (Proverbs 1:7). The wise man skillfully submits to His Lord by applying God's truth to all of life.

be. Does that mean that hard things are not part of life in a fallen world? No, certainly they are, and as we said, being a Christian doesn't immunize you against them. Hard times are the context in which you can be *and* you need to be assured that God is in control, that He is in the problem for good, and your welfare has been purchased at the Cross. Hard times won't reverse or undo what God has done in Christ. That is true hope! The Christian physician, to be truly Christian, must bring to bear these truths upon himself and his patient in the milieu of practicing medicine. God will bless him in the doing (John 13:17; James 1:25).

Let's consider another patient scenario: the patient with the so-called "somatic syndromes," "pain amplification syndromes," or functional pain syndromes such as fibromyalgia, Irritable Bowel Syndrome, multiple chemical sensitivities, certain types of headaches, and chronic fatigue. The literature is voluminous with reports on these conditions, and over the decades "medicine" has assumed the Medical Model of disease. Consequently, theory after theory has been proposed to explain symptoms and the patient's thinking, wanting, and response. Theories abound still, and what is in vogue now is the concept of central sensitization and amplification.[55]

---

55   It is theorized that chemical mediators of the central inhibitory descending pain pathways in patients that carry the diagnosis of fibromyalgia are "defective." It is hypothesized that this "defect" results in augmented

However, to some the Medical Model doesn't do justice to the patient and the medical care system and its many workers. What has been proposed to further "explain" man's problems that fall under the rubric of these conditions are the Biopsychosocial and Biopsychosocialspiritual models (see Appendix A for further discussion). Pain, fatigue, and discomfort are the main symptoms. How do you respond to this patient?

- Many of these patients are some of the most demanding patients whom one sees in his office. Yet they seem oblivious to that fact. The patient can be gracious in her (it is usually a woman, for whatever reason) demands, but nevertheless she does demand. A common demand is an answer to the question "why." Basically she is asking a theological question—one of determinism. However, behind it all she wants to know "why" so she and I can fix it (mostly the physician). Otherwise her alternative is to cope, accept, tolerate, and do the best she can. Those answers underlie a philosophy and theology of life—a worldview. For the Christian physician, "where is God in her thinking?" is a most important first question. Bringing God into the picture (He is already there!) is the first step in helping her get true victory. So I say that I will tell her why.

---

pain processing centrally. These patients "feel" pain (they report that they hurt) when "normal" people don't.

As you remember, our God is the Triune Personal God who is omnipresent—He is man's environment as the Creator, Controller, and Sustainer of the world (Psalm 139). He is actively involved with His creation, including His creatures: His covenantal Lordship (Ephesians 1:11). As Lord of lords and Kings of kings, He called a people to be His and He keeps His promise (1 Peter 1:3-5, 13; 2:4-10). Unfortunately, too many Christian patients, physicians, and pastors don't agree that our God is sovereign over all that comes to pass (Ephesians 1:11-14) or that He is not obligated to use His power to prosper me.

- At this point in the patient-doctor relationship, we don't know the patient. She may not be a Christian, or she may be a Christian who is functioning as if her relationship to Christ had no impact or influence in her life.

- Thinking biblically, you know the problem, but reaching her with it and God's solution is another issue. Most people watch television, read the newspaper, and surf the web. They believe that they are fully aware of what is "out there" in terms of medications and what these "syndromes" really are. They come expecting, even demanding relief and expect you to give it to them.

- So how will you respond? One reason that I developed patient literature (see footnotes 24, 27, 40, 50, and pages 102 and 110) is to help patients address these issues. If

God wants His people to have informed and intelligent faith (and He does!), then it seemed to me that I should follow that model and inform my patients of the facts about arthritis and rheumatism and about themselves as thinking and wanting people who are in an "I don't like" situation by their own choice. These papers and the patient's answers often, but not always, serve as a point of contact for me so that I will be able to present the only truth that frees in a way that is most appropriate for her (John 8:31-36). However, initially, she doesn't know that, and often she has a functional disconnect with biblical truth—her relationship in Christ (if a believer) and her response to life including physical conditions. She has been so habituated to living by feelings (both good and bad ones), that to live by anything else is foreign to her.

- I work hard at getting to know the patient in her situation, trying never to minimize it. I do offer hope— the hope that is present in the gospel, how that hope is hers (if she is a believer), and the significance of living according to that hope. Most patients have never heard biblical truth presented in this way, that a relationship with Christ is not just for the future ("pie in the sky") or for Sunday or the preacher, but for her right *now* and includes addressing physical problems. This truth is captured in 2 Timothy 3:16-17 and 2 Peter 1:3-4, both of which we have previously discussed.

As I have said, a person will live according to Satan's lies or God's truth. As a believer, progressive sanctification includes replacing Satan's lies with God's truth. Only then is a believer truly pleasing God. Proverbs 3:5-8 teaches that is the best thing that he can do for his health.

- I evaluate the condition and state of her body. I order appropriate laboratory data and radiographic material and personally review these with the patient. This personal touch is designed for me to be God's kind of physician and to encourage the patient as a whole person.

- During our discussion, the patient may be incredulous that "nothing" has been found wrong with her body. Helping her see the connection between the physical and spiritual is vital. Unfamiliar to thinking along those lines, she may not be able to identify any specific life-problem that which she thinks "did this to her." However, there is one, and it is major: having a body that she doesn't like and wishing it was gone. In fact, the inner-person dynamic is cyclical: she doesn't like her body, she focuses on bad feelings, bad feelings in *and* from the body are intensified —a constant reminder of her woe — and add to why she doesn't like her body. This dynamic is appropriate for what I call "symptom genesis" and "symptom magnification."

It is interesting how often patients seem to minimize their response to their body as a factor of aggravating their symptoms. The fact that she has approached me with an "I deserve" and "I don't deserve" mentality/mindset is where I start. I know that medication, exercise, and physical therapy are not going to change her mindset. As a result of those treatments, her feelings may change to some degree, but not her thinking. She may say she feels better and therefore her thinking is better, but she still has a body that she doesn't like. And it will act up. She still has the thinking that often times drives more pain and fatigue.

- In such situations, I spend more time with the patient. How much depends on my patient load, the patient before me, and the difficulty of her medical condition. I can take time with patients, in part, because I am specialist. The important point, though, is this: presenting biblical truth appropriately and in some form is a necessary aspect of being a truly Christian physician. How are you doing in this area? If you need help, let your pastor know, or let me know. It bears repeating: have the patient talk with her pastor. But it is critical to know what kind of pastor you refer the patient to. The selection is as critical as for the pastor knowing the type of doctor to whom he will send his sheep. You want a pastor who understands patients biblically and who is willing to help the patient apply biblical truth in order to be God's kind of patient. The wrong kind of pastor can do more harm than good.

Assuming this format of illustration is helpful and in order to fulfill my promise of presenting "how-to" practice medicine as a Christian physician, I will continue to illustrate the application of many of the truths previously discussed. What follows are several patient encounters that are typical in a day in my practice.

Patient #1: Ms. W.

Ms. W is here for a routine follow-up appointment

Doctor: "Hello Ms. W. What's up? How are you doing?"

Ms. W: "It is the same old, same old."

Doctor: "How can that be? God's faithfulness is new every morning, as Jeremiah says in Lamentations 3:23."

Ms. W: "You know what I mean."

Doctor: "No I really don't. Help me understand. I like to think that what God says is true."

Ms. W: "I mean I am still struggling—hurting and so tired. I go to bed tired and hurting, and I awaken the same way."

Doctor: "What are you thinking and wanting when you feel that way?"

Ms. W: "It is that life and my body are the pits. I want relief—even just a little."

Doctor: "Then what happens?"

Ms. W: "I don't get any better. I take my pills and rest a lot. I do my exercises, but it just hurts all the more. I know that I need to exercise, but I just don't feel like it. So I just lay around."

Doctor: "So when relief doesn't come, what then?"

Ms. W: "I take my pills and rest and even pray to God—for relief."

Doctor: "And when relief doesn't come?"

Ms. W: "I take another pill."

Doctor: "How have you responded to God and His temporary or permanent answer of 'no'?"

Ms. W: "I keep praying. I know somehow He will use my body for His glory."

Doctor: "How do you think He will do that?"

Ms. W: "I don't know, but I am waiting."

Doctor: "Remember those verses in Romans 8:28-29? How are you applying them?"

Ms. W: "I think about them. I guess I am supposed to *do* something."

Doctor: "Remember the example of the Christian oyster?"

Ms. W: "Yes, but it is so hard. I just hurt so much. And

when I do try to do something, I hurt more. I need to change, don't I?"

Doctor: "Yes, you do. Would you like for me to help you change?"

Ms. W: "Yes I would."

Doctor: "Great. Here is *why* (humble and joyful thankfulness for the Cross and God's Holy Spirit in you), and here is *how* (I give specific biblical and medical instructions to meet her where she is)."

The story has been changed, but the message and responses are so typical. No matter what the patient's diagnosis is, true help comes only from helping her apply God's truth. In the office, you and I have time constraints. The scenario above, in some form, occurs in less than five minutes. And due to the time constraints, it is of vital importance to know God's truth so that it is "at the ready" for use in the office. Of equal importance is to have some mechanism by which patients can receive more extensive discipling. If you were following the "conversation," you heard an all-so-common statement about God and the believer's relationship with Him. If she didn't get relief, she would pray, and if that didn't get it, she took the next step—a pill to give her what her God had not. That approach to life and to God is of major theological proportions. We must recognize it for what it is and be ready to honor God by practicing biblically-based medicine.

You can do that by discipling her yourself or having her pastor or church leader do so. Another alternative is to send her to some local church that has a truly biblical counseling ministry. An overriding biblical truth is that relief from body problems, including pain and fatigue, may never come in this life, but pleasing God can and does. And when that is the over-riding principle driving one's life, that is true relief.

Patient #2: Ms. P

Here is another patient-doctor dialogue—this time a new patient. She presents with trouble – in many different forms but mostly with complaints of fatigue and pain. She is on multiple medications and has multiple diagnoses.

> Ms. P: "I am here for you to fix me—I hurt, no one can help me, and I hope you can."
>
> Doctor: "What are the problems?"
>
> Ms. P: "I told you—I'm in pain, and I can't take it. I have had health problems all my life—pain, discouragement, and even depression. They say I am bipolar."
>
> Doctor: "Tell me about all of those."
>
> Ms. P: "There is nothing to tell. I get upset, do more, then get down because I hurt and I am tired. And then I don't do anything. I get angry mostly when things don't go my way. And I get down when things are not going right so I hurt some more."

Doctor: "What things are you referring to?"

Ms. P: "Just life—all sorts of things. I should have been treated differently by my parents, my ex-husband, and other doctors. I didn't get want I wanted, and so I get angry and show them a thing or two. But they don't like me very much, and I don't like them, either."

Doctor: "Wow, it sounds like a mess. So, now what?"

Ms. P: "Medications and rest are all I know. I do smoke—it is my friend and the only place I get relief."

Doctor: "What happens if the pain doesn't go away?"

Ms. P: "I will have to live with it, but I won't like it, and I don't want to think about that."

Doctor: "How can I help?"

Ms. P: "*Do* something."

Doctor: "I will. It sounds to me like you are trapped—in bondage, and only the truth will set you free."

Ms. P: "That sounds good—where do we get it?"

Doctor: "I am glad you asked."

I have patients like this who are angry and bitter at God for giving them the body that they have and not the body that they wanted, as well as the spouse that they have and not the spouse that they wanted. Faced with these situations, I am glad that I know that the Bible is the resource that I need for addressing all of the things Ms. P mentioned. If I am going to help Ms. P, I need God's grace and truth. But I have to help her come to that conclusion.

Faced with this situation before, I described a patient in a similar situation in the book, *True Competence in Medicine: Practicing Biblically-based Medicine in a Fallen World*. Mary (not her real name) described in the book, still sees me. She came to understand that life is less about her getting what she wants or about relief and changed circumstances. Life is more about pleasing God, and that perspective has simplified her life. Such can be the case with Ms. P.

Let's look at one final patient—one who has an acute problem. It may be appendicitis, cholecystitis, some infectious process such as tonsillitis or pneumonia, or even a skeletal fracture. Physically, the problem appears to be more localized. The patient may or may not have comorbidity. Sometimes these types of patients are a welcome break from the grind of addressing patients with multiple complaints and no real pathology. So how do you approach this type of patient?

- First, the basic principles of practicing medicine as a Christian that we have been discussing are similar no matter whether the problem is single, acute, or chronic, and has or has not defined pathology and treatment. Ministering to the whole person is still the key to "victorious doctoring."

- These types of patients just don't feel good; often they

have fever and other symptoms and signs related to their respective sites of involvement. Therefore, history taking (data gathering) may be shortened and truncated. However, you can learn much about them by simply observing their responses to the illness. One's actions and inactions may tell you more than words. So look for opportunities to get to know him, to introduce Christ into the treatment plan (especially if he a Christian), do a good job of handling his physical problem, and use your expertise and God's providence to develop a relationship that you can use to move towards a biblical worldview.

- As he improves and is eventually "cured," your goal is to have him use this illness—a failing body—to properly focus vertically. Sometimes a patient may have had illnesses, even a serious one, and been cured and go on to conclude that life is not that bad and failing bodies can and should be fixed. You are to be on the lookout for such a conclusion. Healing is not an inalienable right. In God's providence, some unbelievers are healed, and some believers are not. Your patient's responsibility is to honor God no matter the state of his body by discerning physical problems from God's perspective.

- God's perspective is the only one that counts, and He wants all of His people to agree with it. How will that agreement look? You will bring a certain expertise that God in His providence brought to bear on your patients. By God's grace, chances are good there will be a cure. Remember that physical cure points to a greater spiritual truth—a cleansed heart. So ask your patient what he has learned about himself, God, and others, and how his relationship with Christ has changed. It's more than likely that you are his primary care doctor. He trusts you and probably confides in you. You already have a relationship. Use it wisely to advance God's kingdom.

In all these cases, I address the whole person. That includes the body. Often that is the easiest thing to do. We tend to do what is easy, especially when the time is short, at a premium, and patients are demanding.

Now I will bring many of the principles into focus as I relate the story of Ms. S. She is a composite patient but the type many specialists encounter daily. You may be thinking: "those patients really need a different approach." Just because the patient has chronic and multiple problems and multiple medications doesn't mean this approach won't work. Doctors made those initial diagnoses and began treatment. What I hope that you see, and agree with, is that the principles of practicing as a Christian are fundamentally the same for *all* patients. This one patient helps me bring together some of what I have been saying throughout the book.

Ms. S is a fifty-six-year-old divorced woman who is a smoker (one pack per day) and has long-standing complaints of aches and pains, chronic obstructive pulmonary disease (COPD), diabetes complicated by her obesity, sedentary life, and periodic use of prednisone for her COPD. She presented to me, for the first time, with the request (almost a demand) to help her not hurt so much. She hurts when she walks, sits for any length of time, lies down, and rolls over. She has multiple diagnoses. What do I do?

- I get a history. I start at the beginning. She reports that she has been hurting for thirty years—fifty percent of her life. She says that the chiropractor told her that she was "crooked and out of alignment." She says pain, which she describes as all over, comes and goes with good and bad days. She hurts when she overdoes anything but even more so when she "under does." I find out about "under-doing." She tells me that she has never been asked that question. She answers by saying that she rests a lot—up to six hours per day.

- I ask her about wanting and thinking. She tells me that when life is hard (a hurting body), it is often because she has been doing but not liking it and wondering why she hurts and has the body she does. She tells me that she realizes now that kind of thinking only aggravates her body. She never thought of herself as mechanically inefficient. She says that sounds like she is "getting old."

- Next she tells me that her knees hurt and sometimes swell. Yes, she says, she waddles and has put on weight. "I don't feel like it" is her reason for not working on weight loss—so she eats and doesn't exercise. In our discussion, she tells me that life has been hard for her and lists a number of ways that it is (such as work, lack of finances, and family). She tells me that she is on medications such as antidepressants, anti-anxiolytics and anti-psychotics because she is down, moody, angry at times, and "just wants to punch out of life." She has received diagnoses of depression, panic attacks, and bipolar disorder. She smokes because that gives her "something to do," and "calms me down." She says it is hurting her body, but "she can't help it."

- Her physical examination shows that she is overweight. She has quadriceps muscle atrophy, slight flexion contractures in her knees, and pelvic and scapular tilts, paraspinal muscle tightness, and tight hamstrings. She has prolonged expiration and a rare wheeze.

- Now what? Here is a lady who undoubtedly has osteoarthritis of the knees—a most likely diagnosis given the localized expression of disease, her age, and weight. She also has axial problems and is mechanically inefficient. She has aggravated her physical problems by her thinking, her wanting, and her manner of handling life. She is here for me to help her. The issue for me is how do I define help, and how do I bring it to her?

- I have spent time listening to her, getting to know her in her world and situation, and asking questions that move into the area of motivation—what makes her tick? She does volunteer that she prays and goes to church sometimes. She says that she "knows Jesus," but He has seemed so distant. She adds that may be her fault because she thinks her life should be different. *Perhaps He has let me down*, she muses.

- This is her initial appointment. I have a lot of work to do. I know that Ms. S has a life-long pattern of handling life based on her feelings, considers herself a victim, and is grumbling and complaining against God and His providence. I know that her response to life situations has worsened her body problems. Life has been hard for a variety of reasons. In response, having no readily available biblical truth to interpret the pressures in her life and direct her attitudes and actions has placed her in a dark hole.

- Ms. S agreed that she was in a black hole with nowhere to go. Unless I bring a sovereign good God (you see the importance of knowing proper theology) into the picture, this woman will continue to handle life poorly.

As a result, her physical problems will worsen. I set out a plan. The "pain papers" are helpful here. Information on osteoarthritis of the knee is helpful. I give her an exercise program, one that she can do in her own home, directed at both her knee and her axial problems. I will lay out what can be done after we have a clearer view of her body problems based on radiographs and laboratory exam. She agrees. I then ask her if she will read her Bible. She says yes. I ask her to read John 8:31-36 and tell me what learns. She says she will.

- On her return appointment, Ms. S reports that she has read the five papers, answered the questions, and wonders what happens next. She reiterates that she is a mess and asks if there is any hope. I ask her to define her goal and hope. She musters a smile, saying that I ask a lot of questions, but she is glad that I do. I smile to myself, glad that she knows that I do care.

- We review the radiographs and laboratory data, and it confirms what I expected. She has OA in her knees but still has joint space left on the radiograph; I tell her that she still has "life left in her knees." She can see the "crooked spine" on her radiographs and is amazed that "I am like that."

- I address her "physical" problems by asking if she has done her exercises and note that she has lost one pound.

Then I ask her about John 8. She agrees that she is in bondage and doesn't see any way out. One of the pain papers addresses pain, depression, and pressure. She has read it and wonders too how something outside of her can cause her to feel bad. She realizes that "it can't, except by the way I think." She says she is ready for a change—she wants to feel better.

- After aspirating and injecting her knees, prescribing a non-steroidal agent, and reviewing the exercises—not just the how but the important "why," I ask her to read a pamphlet that is designed to define and to give true hope, entitled "Christ and Your Problems." The booklet unpacks 1 Corinthians 10:13. She is to summarize it in ten lines or less and compare and contrast God's four promises in 1 Corinthians 10:13 with Satan's lies. She finds that interesting and wants hope. I schedule a return visit and offer to see her sooner to discuss the reading material. I encourage her to talk with her pastor.

- At her follow-up visit, she tells me that she is doing her exercises, that she has reread the material, and that she has read the pamphlet. She isn't clear on hope but says she is ready to learn. She says that she is a believer but hasn't always thought or acted like one. She wants to feel better and understands that her previous thinking and wanting have led to complications. I asked her to read Proverbs 13:15, and she relates to the hardness of life that verse points out. Again she is ready for more of God's truth. I ask her what she is willing to do and why. She is tired of "living life on the run" and not getting anywhere. She didn't know how to get off her roller coaster. She does see light—hopefully the Light of the world, Jesus Christ (John 8:12; 9:5).

What I have just described is a demonstration of God's *grand* work in a patient's life—a human being given God's instrument that is unpleasant for her to use in order to grow in Christlikeness. That is true help. How much more I will do is another matter. That depends, in part, on my expertise as a doctor, as a Christian doctor, as a student of Scripture, and time constraints. Ms. S is moving in the right direction. She has a long way to go—so many problems in her life that she has responded to sinfully—but if she stays with a 2 Corinthians 5:9 and Romans 8:28-29 perspective of life, she will continue to grow and change and find that which has been missing in her life. I direct her to either myself, her pastor (I need to know something about him and his view of counseling), or a truly biblical counselor. Perhaps a local church has a counseling ministry. That is part of knowing the resources in your community that I mentioned earlier in the book.

I am going to switch gears at this juncture. So far, this section has focused on the "how-tos" of my view of practicing medicine as a Christian. I emphasized the doctor's personal relationship with the patient and that interaction as a function of his relationship with Christ. There are other aspects of this subject that I need to mention. I will put them in question form. These are a type of checklist, but they also highlight some of the points that I have been making.

- As a Christian, how do you introduce yourself to a patient? How does being a Christian affect your style of greeting, data gathering, note taking, examination, and conversation? I have given examples that emphasize a whole-person exchange moving toward the application of biblical principles in the care of the patient's body.

- What obvious differences stemming from your Christianity strike people who visit you (not only as a patient) and work for you? Moreover, do you consider it a detriment to your practice? You should list the differences in your practice of medicine compared to that of your unbelieving colleague.

- How do you introduce Christianity into the conversation? I have written about this at length. Perhaps you have other ways of bringing Christ into the patient's problem and solution. Share those with Christian physicians, including me, so we can grow together.

- How do you continue the discussion once you have introduced a biblical truth? The response to presenting biblical principles to patients is often "underwhelming." There are a number of reasons for such responses both from the patient and doctor side.

From the patient's side, his response may be colored by his status as an immature believer, as a rebellious believer, or as an unbeliever. He may misunderstand the influence and significance of his relationship with Christ and his physical problems; he may be poorly taught in the general areas of knowing and doing and in the particular area of the Bible and the body. There may be a lack of oversight at his church; and he may have tried and failed to be God's kind of patient, leaving him hopeless.

From the doctor's side, you may have presented the appropriate truth but in a manner that engendered resentment or misunderstanding, or you may have offered truth that did not apply to him in his situation. You may have misunderstood the significance of your relationship with him and really didn't know him, or you may not have laid the foundation sufficiently to help him want the true gift of life. Remember that you may be the only person who feeds him real medicine—the bread of life.

- How do you go about telling people bad news as well as the good news? Is God's providence part of the answer? As I have emphasized throughout, our God is Creator, Controller, and Sustainer of His world His way.

A response to physical problems is a response to Him and His control. This truth is underemphasized, even neglected. Once you and your patient get a hold of the truth of God's good control, you and he will never be the same.

Part of the "bad news" is the state of his health, humanly speaking—conditions such as end-stage renal, cardiac, or lung disease. The end results in these diseases may be death. How do you help your patients? There are a multitude of resources to utilize. Do you know your local hospice service and what it teaches? Do they present Christ and if so, how? I have referenced my book and pamphlet on grief that is one resource on the subject (see footnote 27 and appendix C). But more so, do you know the Bible's teaching on death, and are you willing to present it to your patient and his family? Death will always be with us until Jesus returns. Our population is getting older. We will have plenty of opportunities to minister to dying patients and their families. We need to be ready. And one way to help Christians do that is help them live well—with an eternal perspective. Heaven is the believer's destination; we are only pilgrims on this earth.

- How do you meet objections both by the Christian and non-Christian to overt statements about the Christian faith, especially when you present biblical principles? You will meet opposition; Jesus did, so will His follow-

ers (John 15:18-21; 2 Timothy 3:12; also see Matthew
10:17-18; 1 Peter 4:12; 5:9).

If the world hates you, keep in mind that it hated me
first. If you belong to the world, it would love you
as its own. As it is, you do not belong to the world,
but I have chosen you out of the world. That is why
the world hates you. Remember the words I spoke to
you: "No servant is greater than his master. If they
persecuted me, they will persecute you also. If they
obeyed my teaching, they will obey yours also. They
will treat you this way because of my name for they
do not know the One who sent me.

(John 15:18-21)

In fact, everyone who wants to live a godly life in
Christ Jesus will be persecuted.

(2 Timothy 3:12)

The mindset of the believer and non-believer are antithet-
ical—they are opposed to each other. Therefore, when you
present God's truth—assuming it is His truth that is given
in a gracious and clear manner—to the unbeliever (or a believer who is functioning like an unbeliever), you can expect
resistance. The culture's hatred is not and must not be due to
what Jesus' disciples do wrong, but what they do right —in

this case, teaching the patient to be God's kind of patient for the proper reason. As I have pointed out, we are only messengers, and as messengers, we are to reflect the Message Sender—our triune Personal God. Make sure it is not you whom patients resist. Our goal is to please God, and, as I have emphasized, we do that by gently but clearly and accurately presenting appropriate biblical principles and helping the patient implement them.

- When a patient sins, what do you say in response? I presented a patient encounter that discussed this subject. If the preaching of sin is missing from the majority of our pulpits, and I think that it is, so is the gift and grace of repentance (Matthew 3:7-8; Acts 11:18). It shouldn't be that way in the office of the Christian physician. We don't have space to unfold the Bible's teaching on repentance. As I have pointed out, it must be explained to the patient (and maybe his pastor). Suffice it to say here that sin and its remission is why Jesus came into the world as the God-man. Sin is serious—the Cross proves it. Your view of sin is a reflection of your view of God, Christ, and self. If sin is no "big deal" in your thinking, then you have changed the definition of God, Christ, and the Cross. And you have a view of self and God that is counter to the Bible's teaching about both. If sin is serious, so too is repentance—and they are!

The word means to change one's thinking—get it in line with God's. And a lot of what I have been talking about is to help bring that change about. It is not only an "about face" in terms of thinking and desires but of actions as well. It is associated with fruit (Matthew 3:8: Produce fruit in keeping with repentance... ; Luke 3:8: Produce fruit in keeping with repentance...). One fruit of repentance is putting on good stewardship out of gratitude for the Cross.

• What does your office communicate to the patient? Does it communicate warmth and a willingness to spend time to answer questions and to resolve difficulties, or does it communicate a coldness and a desire to move patients "through" as quickly as possible? And a corollary question: what relationships to office personnel that are obvious to patients indicate that your office is a different sort of place? Office and personnel are extensions of you. They reflect you as you reflect Christ. This area of patient care is important. It is less important when you are in a group, especially a large one, and one that doesn't identify itself as Christian. There are a myriad of ways to let patients know that your first allegiance is to the Lordship of Jesus Christ and to the degree that you do, you will help the patient function as God's kind of patient. But you must work at finding and learning how. That effort itself should be a blessing to you, your office personnel, and the patient. Perhaps more on this at a later time.

- How does your new patient and return visit policy differ from that of an unbeliever? Interesting question. As physicians, we are moving into a time of reimbursement cuts. Our services may be socialized as the demand for the same level of patient care increases or at least remains high. How will you address that issue from a Christian perspective? Balancing good business practices and the biblical truth that medicine is a ministry takes wisdom, ingenuity, and courage.

- How are your referral policies affected by your faith? This is also an interesting question. I addressed the topic in my book: *True Competence on Medicine: Practicing Biblically-Based Medicine in a Fallen World*. I do refer patients to unbelievers. Sometimes they are better listeners, and patients are apt to come away from the visit understanding what was said. Sometimes the unbeliever is the most skillful in handling the patient's physical problem (such as a total hip or knee replacement). I do caution, even warn, my patient who is a believer. I encourage him to be ready to hear a non-biblical approach to medicine and his problem and to be ready to evangelize the doctor, primarily by being God's kind of patient and praying for him.

- When you complete an office visit, how do you close it? Do you have any parting advice for the patient? I know that some physicians pray with their patients. Prayer is another subject worth studying. I have commented on it several times in the book. Prayer is an expression of our dependence on God and humble submission to Him (He tells us to pray). Not only that, but praying also models Christ, who prayed regularly and taught others how to pray. But prayer is not the key—the key is the God of prayer. Sometimes it is easy to pray and hard to bring God's truth to the patient in a concrete fashion. The subject of your prayer is very important. Let me encourage you to pray, not so much for healing, but for you and the patient to honor God as His kind of doctor and patient. God bless as you do.

Conclusion

WELL, THERE YOU HAVE IT. We began our journey into a Christian view of practicing medicine by introducing reasons for calling attention to the need for doctors to practice medicine as Christians. One of the foundational reasons was historical: medicine is rooted in and steeped in pagan thinking; consequently, it offers no proper vertical reference to life or for life. In contrast, by the culture's standard, both believing and non-believing physicians can practice "good" medicine. The key was to define "good," and that meant we needed a standard. The culture's call to practice "good" medicine or ethical medicine stands in marked contrast to the Bible's call to Christian physicians. That call consists of ministering to patients from the "inside out" in whatever context the person finds himself (in our case, physical problems) in Christ's name for His glory. The patient's physical problem is the context in which you address the impact of his, and your, relationship to Christ. Ministry is the key for the practice of medicine if one desires to practice as God's kind of doctor.

To be Christian, your ministry must have both a *proper* vertical and horizontal orientation to life and to the practice for medicine. Vertically (downward), the doctor and patient are loved by God (1 John 4:19). For the doctor, a proper vertical orientation (upward) means that first and foremost, he is motivated by Christ's love for him. In response to that love, the doctor seeks to please God out of thankfulness for the Cross, his salvation, and growth in Christ—he cares for the patient God's way out of a proper horizontal orientation of life. He will then minister, not only as a "body" or "spiritual mechanic," but as a person who ministers to the whole person.

Horizontally, the doctor will then help the patient be God's kind of patient by providing good care of his body but never divorcing the outer and inner man. Creationally, God has linked the two, and what He has linked together no man, especially the doctor, dare separate. We discussed the significance of God's design in a number of ways, one of which is captured in this phrase: wanting and thinking influence feeling and doing so that a person is not simply feelings. Those feelings originate from within and manifest a desire to please God or to get for oneself, even good health or relief. In all patient-doctor relationships, irrespective of the body problem, honoring God as a good theologian-steward is the fulfillment of 2 Corinthians 5:9 and Colossians 3:17 for both physician and patient.

Biblically-based medical care as I have defined it is misunderstood and I fear almost non-existent. We labored to define it, and we determined that although the Bible is not a medical textbook, it is all that you need to practice medicine in a God-pleasing manner. How so? The Bible requires you to be efficient in knowledge and skills. In addition, your practice of medicine, your science, and your worldview must be informed and directed, even groomed, by biblical principles. The Bible is God's Word, which is His powerful and purposeful self-expression. In it, God, the Creator, Controller, and Sustainer of all of life is talking to His people—to you. When God speaks, we *must* listen and respond according to His Word. We have no business re-interpreting His Word to suit ourselves. Therefore, when God's truth and "science" seem to be at odds, you must come down on God's side. That requires an understanding *and* application of biblical truth in major areas such as failing bodies, answering the "why me" questions from both believers and unbelievers, and death and dying. The Bible is God's Owner's manual for life—His gift to you and your patient. As a Christian, your privilege and obligation is to use it well. Daily.

God has set you apart as His physician in order to practice medicine His way. Pleasing Him is what life is to be all about—in and outside the office. Re-interpreting all of life, including the practice of medicine, is a must for all Christians. A proper vertical reference means to think God's thoughts after Him by bringing biblical principles to bear on the patient in terms of diagnosis and treatment of his problem. Therefore, as a Christian physician, you will minister to the whole patient, inside out. In that way you will honor God. When that happens, your patient is most benefited, and you will have advanced God's kingdom. Praise God as you practice His way for His glory.

APPENDIX A

Theories of disease

I. **Medical Model (MM): It is *presumed* that the body is sick and that symptoms, as well as signs and behavior, are caused by an abnormality in some organ or tissue, causing malfunction of the body (molecular model of disease). This would include mental illness.**

   A. Under the MM, disease is *diagnosed* when discoverable abnormalities are present by some objective testing, and symptoms can be explained on the basis of these abnormalities.

   B. A person's thoughts, beliefs, and desires are considered to be *independent* of the diagnosis and management of the patient. (Some call this a "mind-body dualism.")

   C. A *therapeutic* rationale is developed as a result.

   D. The MM has been quite successful in the diagnosis and management of certain diseases, especially those that are acute. In those cases, the focus is usually on a single, acute medical problem, e.g., streptococcal pharyngitis, appendicitis, pneumonia, or lung cancer.

E. There is no room for God in this model. In fact, the model developed as a reaction against the mysticism and superstition prevalent in the medieval age.

II. **Biopsychosocial Model (BPS): Since the early 1990s, medicine has moved toward the more inclusive BPS model of disease and patient care, emphasizing the role and importance of biology, psychological factors, and environmental factors on health and bodily function.**

A. These factors are considered *determinants* of the condition and include genes, biology, and outside pressure.

B. These factors "do" it to a pre-programmed person so that he feels and acts a certain way.

1. *Biological* refers to a person's genetic makeup (genes) and biochemistry: nature

2. *Psychological* has to do with one's psyche: nature and/or nurture

   a. It is generally defined as one's mind, how he feels, and his *deep* (Freudian term) inner self which are his "inside" environment.

   b. *Psychological disease* and *mental illness* are claimed to indicate that something is wrong in *or* with the brain and mind, which are considered synonymous.

C. *Social* (or environmental): nurture – the term is used in relation to pressure outside the person "causing" something within a person even though "it" is not always measurable.

D. The person's response is measurable and observable and is attributed to that which is outside the person.

1. The individual is never seen as a responsible responder but as a victim.

2. Examples: situational depression, social anxiety

E. There is a *compartmentalization* of the person, leading to the development of "experts" in the fields of social science and physical science who believe that their "area" of the person has a determining influence on the production of physical problems that is called disease and illness. This sets in motion a compartmentalized/holistic treatment program.

III. **Biopsychosocial Spiritual Model (BPSS): The model adds a spiritual dimension to the presumed cause of symptoms, conditions, and disease.**

A. The proponents of this model suggest that at the very least, spiritual variables (however defined) are fundamental determinants of psychological variables, which in turn are determinants of physical and social factors.

B. The major thought is that all these factors play a role in producing or aggravating disease.

C. Proponents cite the *failure* to address spiritual needs of the patient as being linked to patient dissatisfaction and poor clinical outcomes, despite advances in technology and breakthrough treatments.

D. *Spiritual needs* are defined as a *need* to make sense of, give purpose to, and ascribe meaning to illness/life; as a desire to acknowledge and cope with the notion of death/dying; and as a desire to feel in control (or give up control), be connected, and cared for.

E. In this model, the standard for spirituality is never Scripture.

F. The term *spirituality* is used relationally in the context of a person's "connectedness" with self, others, a higher being, or the universe. It is a user-friendly word that includes all religions.

Summary and Critique:

I. **Even though only the MM seeks to demonstrate a physical abnormality as the cause of disease, all three models claim that symptoms originate from some alleged physical defect.**

A. A pathological abnormality often cannot be found or, if present, can't readily explain the person's symptoms.

B. Still, diagnosis and therapy are based on the presence of symptoms, behavior, and the desire for relief rather than correcting a proven, objective malfunction of the body.

C. In the BPS and BPSS models, as part of an overall treatment plan, attention is given to each "compartment" of the person and by a different expert (the physician for the biological, the psychiatrist/psychologist for the psychological, the pastor for the spiritual, and social worker/psychologist for the social).

D. The reasoning: because man is the sum of all these parts and no one person can adequately have all the answers, attention must be given to each part by a different "expert."

II. **Critique: Each of the models excludes God, His judgment, His grace, and His providence. They are theologically incorrect—false.**

A. The MM originally attempted to give an accurate description of an observed phenomenon. It did so in many instances.

B. Today, it is used to explain any and all behavior even when no pathological findings are demonstrated. It paints man as physical only, thereby rejecting the duplex nature of man.

C. The MM champions science as if the God of science and science are opposed.

D. The BPS and the BPSS are attempts to "fill in the gap"

left by the MM. They emphasize a person's psyche, and they move further down the path of wrong theology.

APPENDIX B

The Questionnaire

Introduction:

Hi! Thanks so much for spending time with me. I am trying to get a sense of where MDs are in bringing their Christianity into the office. I am trying to lay a foundation for a book that addresses this topic. I am here only to listen and take notes. I am very interested in what you have to say. I would like to know:

1. Do MDs bring their Christianity into the workplace?
2. How do they do it? What does it look like?
3. What is the reason they do?
4. Is there something more beneficial that we should be doing?

So here is the topic: how do you model your Christian faith in your practice? Please carefully consider the questions below and answer them either in writing or verbally—if verbally, I can write your answers for you. This will help me as I talk to other physicians.

1. What does being a Christian in your daily medical practice mean to you? And please tell me how you define the term *Christian*.

2. Do you connect your Christianity and your relationship with Christ in your medical practice?

    a. Why or why not?

    b. How do you do so?

    c. What are/have been the results?

3. Does knowing the spiritual condition of your patients influence your medical care of them?

    a. Why or why not?

    b. If so, how?

4. How do you help people/patients handle the difficulties of life presented by physical problems?

5. Do you think there is a place for the Word of God to be used in the practice of medicine?

6. Does the Word of God/biblical principles influence how you take care of your patients, and if so, how?

7. Do you use the Bible in helping patients address the unpleasantness of various health problems?

    a. Why or why not?

    b. If so, how and what have been the results?

Thanks again for your time and help with this project.

May God bless each of us and our families as we seek to serve Him.

APPENDIX C

Until Jesus returns, every physician at one time or another will be called on to minister to people who are in their "last days." Physical death is part of God's curse on sin, and God has not chosen to reverse the curse in this life. Therefore, physicians should clearly understand and apply the Bible's teaching on the subject of death and dying. The teaching found in 1 Thessalonians 4 and 2 Corinthians 5 is particularly designed by God to provide help and comfort for His people (2 Corinthians 1:3-4). For these reasons, I have included a discussion of them.

1 Thessalonians 4:13-18

> *Brothers, we don't want you to be ignorant about those who fall asleep or to grieve like the rest of men, who have no hope. We believe that Jesus died and*

rose again and so we believe that God will bring with Jesus those who have fallen asleep in him. According to God's own word, we tell you that we who are still alive, who are left till the coming of the Lord, will certainly not precede those who have fallen asleep. For the Lord himself will come down from heaven, with a loud command, with the voice of the archangel and with the trumpet call of God and the dead in Christ will rise first. After that, we who are still alive and left will be caught up together with them in the clouds to meet the Lord in the air. And so we will be with the Lord forever. Therefore encourage each other with these words.

In the case of the Thessalonians, they had been exposed to false teaching about several issues, including the last days. The false teachers had said that no Christian would die before the second coming of Christ. Yet people were dying, and Jesus had not returned. Among the many dangers presented by this teaching was the lack of hope. Throughout the letter, Paul stresses hope (1:3-5; 2:11-13, 19; 3:3-9). Hope is always in Christ and is based on the promises of a trustworthy, good God.

Paul begins this section with a familiar desire of his: he did not want his readers to be ignorant or uninformed. In particular, he is speaking about death and Christ's return (v.13). Paul knew that truth comforts and encourages and that error confuses and complicates. His goal in informing them was so that they would grieve in a godly manner—with hope. Paul was protecting his flock. They were ignorant and in danger of functioning as unbelievers—grieving without hope. Godly grieving is not self-centered but God-centered. Feeling helpless and hopeless, a person may choose to cease functioning. The secular world calls this *depression*. The biblical understanding of this "emotional" state is giving in to feelings and giving up on responsible living. Proper understanding and application of God's Word is essential to proper grieving.

The specific truth that would enable the Thessalonians to grieve with hope is given in verse 14: "We believe that Jesus died and rose again and so we believe that God will bring with Jesus those who have fallen asleep in Him." Paul's solution for God-dishonoring grieving was to focus on the resurrection. Because Jesus died and rose, so too will the believer. Those who have died in the Lord and those who are alive at the coming of Christ will both be raised together into the newness of life. Neither group has an advantage or disadvantage (v.15). The false teachers were just that—false. Paul taught an eternal perspective of life. The believer is to anticipate the coming of Christ. At that time the dead will rise in Christ (v.16) so that all believers will be with Christ (v.17). Paul is expressing both individual and family joy. To counter the false teaching regarding the last days, Paul pointed his people to the believer's chief hope: Christ and a relationship with Him (5:10; 2 Corinthians 5:8; Philippians 1:23). He closes this section with an exhortation to all those who had lost loved ones: encourage one another with the truth of Christ's second coming for all of His people (v.18). So too are we to present God's truth today.

2 Corinthians 5:1-9:

> *Now we know that if the earthly tent we live in is destroyed, we have a building from God, an eternal house in heaven, not built by human hands. Meanwhile we groan, longing to be clothed with our heavenly dwelling, Because when we are clothed, we will not be found naked. For while we are in this tent, we groan and are burdened, because we do not wish to be unclothed but to be clothed with our heavenly dwelling, so that what is mortal may be swallowed up by life. Now it is God who has made us for this very purpose and has given us the Spirit as a deposit, guaranteeing what is to come. Therefore we are always confident and know that as long as we are at home in the body, we are away from the Lord. We live by faith, not by sight. We are confident, I say, and would*

prefer to be away from the body and at home with the Lord. So we make it our goal to please him, whether we are at home in the body or away from it.

Paul concluded chapter 4 (v.16-18) with a reference to the present and sad condition of the body. He contrasted the outer-man reality of decay with inner-man renewal and the glory that awaits all believers. He then focused on the radical changes and non-negotiable truths that will occur at death and resurrection. He continued to speak of the body (he used the following metaphors: tent, house, and building) in the context of its eventual destruction. However, in the resurrection it will be a radically different body given to him by God. It will be eternal (verse 1); our present physical bodies are only temporary. In verse 2 Paul tells us that day has not arrived for him and his readers. While we wait, we groan. Here the word translated as groan (*stenazo*) indicates a burden from the distress of failing bodies. Groaning is not necessarily wrong (much like grieving in 1 Thessalonians 4). It is wrong when it is selfishly motivated by a longing to leave this earth before God's time. It is not an escapist mindset but an anticipation of receiving the heavenly body that God has promised. Consequently, Paul looks forward to a reclothing (verse 3). Yet, on this earth, we experience and are burdened by the misery of our deteriorating bodies.

Paul makes it clear that the unclothing process (dying and entering into a state of disembodiment) is not something that we look forward to (verse 4). Illness and dying are not natural; they are part of God's curse. So we do groan. But the hope of the Christian is not death and the intermediate, disembodied state. That is only the beginning and an interlude. The resurrection, when body and spirit are reunited in the presence of God, is when all things will be righted. As a guarantee of our eternal existence, God has given us the Holy Spirit. He is the down payment on the heavenly state purchased by Christ for believers (verse 5). As a result, we are to be confident about the future, which affects present living no matter the condition of our body (verse 6).

Paul then draws a contrast: the believer lives by saving faith and biblical principles rather than feelings, his own reasoning, and experiences (verse 7). Saving faith has a forward, vertical reference to life. We do not yet "see" (that which we take in by our senses) the joys of resurrected living, but we look forward to it with joyful certainty because we are in Christ.

Verses 8-9 are designed, in part, to help the believer rekindle hope. They offer help for some of the toughest times in life. They point the clear way to victory. In verse 9, Paul highlights the fact that the goal of life is the same on earth as in heaven: it is to please God. God deserves to be pleased. The reality of resurrection life provides a proper focus for all believers in their decaying bodies to live as God-pleasers and God-trusters.

APPENDIX D

Sleep

SLEEP: GOD'S GIFT — HOW do you think about it?

Man is a sleeping being. Only God doesn't sleep. A person can't go indefinitely without sleep. Try as he might, there will be a time when he will fall asleep. From these facts, it is reasonable to say that sleep is natural; it is God's ordained way of good stewardship of the body as it is important for good health and survival. However, in today's culture there are many people who report that getting to sleep or remaining asleep is difficult or impossible. The culture has offered a variety of reasons for this, and these reasons are matched by the multitude of so-called sleep aides.

I. Physiology of sleep

A. Physiological studies indicate that sleep is both an active and passive process.

B. During sleep, brain activity varies but never stops.

C. Various chemicals are secreted by certain glands that affect sleep (for instance, the pineal gland secretes mela-tonin, which is thought to be a natural sleep inducer—it affects the sleep center).

1. These chemicals are said to ebb and flow throughout the sleep cycle.

2. In terms of sleep disturbances (too little, difficulty going to and staying asleep), it is theorized/suggested that there is a "chemical imbalance."

   a. However, these levels aren't routinely measured, AND no one knows what a "normal" level is.

   b. Even if the level of these chemicals could be mea-sured and shown to be "abnormal," there is a lingering question of which came first: the ab-normal chemical level and the sleep problem or vice versa.

   c. This is a critical point because all types of "sleep aides," including medications, good "hygiene" techniques, and cognitive behavioral therapy are reported to "put you to sleep" by changing this or that chemical.

D. Sleep is actually a mixture of passive phases and active phases. Many of the body's systems may be at rest, while others are hard at work making sure that the sleep cycle progresses as it should.

1. Sleep occurs in levels, but the two main ones are

NREM and REM sleep.

2. NREM sleep, which means non-rapid eye movement, is divided into four progressive categories, and it occurs during most of the sleep cycle. During this part of the sleep cycle, the individuals move into sleep and may well be unconscious, but there are no eye movements or dreams.

3. REM sleep occurs at the end of the sleep cycle, and it is an extremely important part of sleep.

   a. In REM sleep, the neurons in the spinal cord shut off, which in turn causes a temporary paralysis of the muscles in the extremities.

   b. Most average adults will spend two hours in REM sleep. REM sleep is known to motivate the areas of the brain that are connected to learning.

   c. Dreaming occurs during REM sleep.

E. The sleep "switch" area is considered to be in the anterior hypothalamus—the body's "master clock." It is the body's main sleep center, and the posterior hypothalamus is the body's main wake center.

   1. The anterior hypothalamus becomes active during sleep and uses the *inhibitory* neurotransmitters GABA and galanin to initiate sleep by inhibiting the arousal regions of the brain (certain other areas of the brain are wake-promoting regions). Others neurons in the

lateral hypothalamus help stabilize this switch.

2. Multiple neurotransmitters and a balance of their interactions are thought to play a role in sleep: serotonin, nor-epinephrine, acetylcholine, and histamine; dopamine is thought to be associated with wakefulness.

3. Medications are reported to cause a person to fall asleep by turning off the arousal area of the brain and/or turning on the sleep center.

4. Most sleep meds turn off the arousal center by binding to a receptor in the brain (GABA or melatonin receptor), which releases GABA, which inhibits the activity of arousal. Some medications are reported to have a more selective binding than others.

   a. Benzodiazepines: Dalmane, Doral, Halicon, Prosom, Restoril

   b. Non-benzodiazepines: Ambien, Sonata, Lunesta

   c. Antidepressants

   d. Antihistamines

   e. Dopaminergic agents

   f. Rozermem

F. So, as interesting as these facts are, they view sleep strictly as a behavior and physical activity.

1. As you read the sleep literature, several trends and

mottos stand out.

a. Insomnia isn't your fault.

b. You can do something about it.

c. The goal of sleep therapy is to get sleep.

2. These mottos suggest that if you are not sleeping, somehow life is cheating you, and you are not getting what you deserve. In other words, self takes center stage.

3. Most sleep programs report a fifty percent remission rate of insomnia and start with teaching "good sleep hygiene."

   a. The essentials can be summarized under the heading of good stewardship: avoid stimulants especially before bedtime, avoid "clock watching" and "struggling" to get to sleep, get adequate exercise, and utilize proper scheduling of sleep and activity.

   b. Cognitive behavioral therapy, biofeedback, and progressive muscle relaxation

4. The results of various kinds of sleep aides and sleep programs are less than spectacular. And the sleep aides often require chronic use.

5. Where else can we go for help? Since God is the One who created and designed man, it makes sense to look in the Bible for His help.

II. God's answers

A. Sleep is God's gift to man and an integral part of his being.

B. What is your response to that fact?

C. Thankfulness is always in order for God's blessings (Ephesians 5:20; 1 Thessalonians 5:18) — Phil 4:8 (think list): combine think and thank list (2 Corinthians 10:5)

D. The believer's goal in this life is to please God by growing in Christ-likeness: 2 Corinthians 5:9.

  1. One way to become like Christ is to pray and be thankful, with or without sleep.

  2. Being a good steward of what God has given you models Christ.

E. If someone is not sleeping, he needs to determine how his thinking about life, including situations and others, God, and himself, might interfere with what God has intended to be good—in this case, sleep.

  1. His or her identity

  2. Agenda and pursuit of that agenda

III. Psalm 132:4-5 and Proverbs 6:4 speak to priorities in life. Things left undone do influence thinking, which influences sleep and non sleep.

A. **Psalm 132:4-5**: I will allow no sleep to my eyes, no slumber to my eyelids till I find a place for the Lord, a dwelling for the Mighty One of Jacob.

B. **Proverbs 6:4**: Allow no sleep to your eyes, no slumber to your eyelids.

1. Is God suggesting sleep deprivation until a job is done? No, but He is emphasizing priorities—first things first.

2. In Psalm 132, David was responsible for bringing the ark to Jerusalem.

3. In Proverbs 6, the author is warning against folly/foolishness.

4. God's answer in both cases was perseverance and vigilance.

5. So when sleep is hard to come by, ask yourself if you have left God's things undone.

6. And if so, what are they, and how do you plan to fulfill your responsibilities? Make pleasing God your priority (Matthew 6:33), and sleep will be a byproduct.

IV. The sleep of the working man is sweet (Ecclesiastes 5:12). When sleep is not sweet, ask yourself:

A. About your work: what do you do outside the home, and what do you do inside as well?

B. About your working: are you or are you not, and why or why not?

C. About your work at the workplace or at home, and those you work for and with: what are your attitudes toward your work, co-workers, and employers?

D. Your approach to work and to your coworkers: what has been the result of your attitude toward work?

V. David the psalmist sleeps peacefully, even in tough times, because the Lord is his.

Psalm 3:5-6: I lie down and sleep, I wake again because the Lord sustains me. I will not fear the tens of thousands drawn up against me on every side.

Psalm 4:8: I will lie down and sleep in peace for you alone, O Lord, make me dwell in safety.

A. What is David's key to sleep? It is his view of life through his understanding of God.

1. If God is in control—and He is—and His control is good—it is—David concludes, "I am not fearful." He enjoyed sweet sleep.

2. David's confidence/trust is first in the Lord, and sleep is a byproduct of that confidence.

B. He knows that his help and deliverance comes from the Lord (**Psalm 3:8**) who is his refuge and strength (**Psalm 18:1-3; 46:**1).

VI. The Lord grants sleep to those whom He loves (Psalm 127:1-2).

Psalm 127:1-2: Unless the Lord builds the house, its builders labor in vain. Unless the Lord watches over the city, the watchmen guard in vain. In vain you rise early and stay up late, toiling for food to eat – for he grants sleep to those he loves.

  A. The psalmist speaks of the futility of life without a proper vertical reference. The psalmist describes two daily human activities:

    1. Creating – building, making, and earning

    2. Conserving – watching over, keeping, and saving

  B. He concludes that life is either meaningful or useless. Only when a person focuses on God and His truth for direction will life be meaningful. Work and life without God are useless.

  C. Blessings come in the doing—following God's direction for His glory. Otherwise, human efforts are a liability, not an asset.

  D. A good harvest (production) is not the result of endless, human effort but a blessing from God.

  E. Working harder can mean enslavement—more bondage.

  F. The psalmist contrasts sleep (it is a blessing from God) and hurried, frantic work activity without a proper godly reference (the latter is a liability resulting in turmoil/anguish within the heart).

  G. In contrast, sweet sleep is God's gift when the person is in proper relationship to God: solving problems His way, working and resting for His glory, and being thankful for who He is (not what He gives).

VII. Trouble sleeping?

A. If so, then consider God's supreme demonstration of His love: the Cross.

B. How does that fact impact your ability or inability to sleep—to use God's blessing as a gift?

C. Sleep is both a bodily function (a brain "thing") and an inner-man activity (heart).

　　1. What holds a person's thinking affects his activity—including sleeping and not sleeping. As with any other activity, thinking, wanting, desiring, and action are linked.

　　2. So ask:

　　　　a. What are your thoughts on the reason for not sleeping?

　　　　b. What makes it important to sleep?

　　　　c. How do you respond (to self, others, and to God) if you don't sleep?

　　　　d. If you are not sleeping, what is your focus?

D. Biblical "sleep aides"

　　1. Solve problems biblically: daily, consistently, for God's glory

　　2. "Turn off" the day's problems when you go to bed

　　3. By asking:

　　　　a. What thinking is most prominent throughout the day? Give the order of priority in terms of thinking.

b. What is the last thought at bedtime AND the thought that just precedes that last thought? What is your response to them?

c. What is your first thought upon awakening, no matter the time of awakening?

4. Too often the goal is to get sleep rather than please God.

a. God knows that you need sleep—He gave it to you as His gift.

b. There may be things that you are doing or not doing to cause your sleep problems.

c. God calls you to focus on first things first: do a spiritual inventory and determine your responsibilities and your response to them. Also determine any unresolved problems and your response to them.

d. If there are "undone" things, then determine to develop a plan the next day to solve the problem. Don't begin the work that night.

e. Remember to begin the work: plan the work and work the plan. God's blessings come in the doing.

5. The more you focus on your problem, problem solving, or getting to sleep, the more elusive sleep becomes.

a. The key is getting your focus off self and on God.

b. Instead, use that time to focus on pleasing God by meditating on God and His Word and trusting in His promises.

Summary: God knows what you need. He designed your body and has given sleep as His gift to you. Use it wisely. When you are not sleeping, go to another of God's gifts to you: His Word. Discover what the Creator and Designer of your body says about sleep. Blessings will flow to you as you do!

For more information about
Dr. Jim Halla
&

Being Christian in Your Medical Practice
please visit:

www.JimHalla.com
JimHalla@gmail.com
facebook.com/JimHalla

....

For more information about
AMBASSADOR INTERNATIONAL
please visit:

www.ambassador-international.com
@AmbassadorIntl
www.facebook.com/AmbassadorIntl